James
Oglethorpe

Young Defender

Illustrated by Maurice Rawson

James
Oglethorpe

Young Defender

by Aileen Wells Parks

THE **BOBBS-MERRILL** COMPANY, INC.
A SUBSIDIARY OF HOWARD W. SAMS & CO., INC.
Publishers · INDIANAPOLIS · NEW YORK

LIBRARY OF CONGRESS CATALOG CARD NUMBER: 60-7711

PRINTED IN THE UNITED STATES OF AMERICA

For Edd

Illustrations

Full pages

Numerous smaller illustrations

Contents

Books by Aileen Wells Parks

BEDFORD FORREST: BOY ON HORSEBACK
DAVY CROCKETT: YOUNG RIFLEMAN
JAMES OGLETHORPE: YOUNG DEFENDER

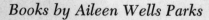

★ # James
Oglethorpe

Young Defender

"Watch That Ram!"

ALMOST seven-year-old Jamie Oglethorpe bent over with his hands on his knees to look closely at the puppies.

"One, two, three, four spotted puppies," he crooned to himself, "and this teeny little white one."

Jamie touched the white puppy. His fur was soft but sleek. "I'll take this one and show him to Nannie and Fanny and Molly," he decided.

Tammie, the mother dog, raised her head quickly. She growled deep in her throat. She stood up, and the puppies tumbled back on the straw in the box.

Old Tofts, the coachman, strolled over. "Better not play with them yet, Master Jamie," he said. "When they get bigger Tammie won't mind."

The fat little puppies were lost without their mother's warm body to nuzzle. They scrambled in all directions, whimpering softly.

"Oh, Tofts," Jamie cried, "they can't see! Are they blind?"

Tofts chuckled. "All puppies are blind when they are two days old," he said. "They'll be good sheep dogs. Just like their mother."

"Can I take one tomorrow?" Jamie demanded.

"Nay, now, laddie. Not so soon."

Jamie put his hand on Tammie's head. "I won't hurt your puppies." He pulled the dog's ears gently and scratched the top of her head.

He looked up at Tofts. "I like living in the country," he told the man. "It's ever so much nicer than London."

12

"Aye, laddie," agreed Tofts. "It is good to have the family in the manor house again. Come see Sandy before you go back to the house."

Jamie had been at Westbrook Place only a few weeks. He had been born in London in December, 1696. Except for a year at Westbrook Place when he was three, he had always lived in the city.

It had been exciting to meet the families who lived in the small thatched cottages on the farm and to find they all knew he was James Edward Oglethorpe. He liked to watch the men at work: to see them trim the yew trees in the gardens, to follow them in the orchard as they gathered apples, to stand back as they chopped firewood, and to go to the stable with Tofts.

Today Jamie walked back into the stable beside the old coachman. The horses were eating hay. First there was Scimitar. He was a fine saddle horse that belonged to Jamie's brother

Lewis. Then came Unicorn and Spider, Lady Oglethorpe's carriage horses.

Sandy was in a stall by himself. He was a small roan with a white star on his forehead.

Tofts whistled, and Sandy raised his head. He took a step forward and stretched his neck over the low door of the stall. He looked at Tofts and then bent down to snuffle at the boy.

"He knows me, Tofts!" Jamie said. "See, he does! I knew he would!"

14

"To be sure he knows you, Master Jamie," Tofts agreed.

Jamie reached up and stroked the white star on the horse's forehead. "Pretty Sandy. Fine boy, Sandy," he said. "I'm going to ride you a lot this year."

"Better run back now, so Nurse Middlecase won't be cross," Tofts suggested.

"Nannie said I could come to the stable to see Tammie," Jamie said. He gave Sandy a final pat.

Outside the dark stable the day was still bright. The sun's rays hit puddles of water and made them sparkle. The dark leaves of the hedge around the stableyard glistened.

There were loud noises in the lane.

"Coo-ey, coo-ey," voices called.

"Arf! arf! arf!" a dog barked.

"Baa, baa-ah, baa-a-ah," sheep answered.

Jamie ran to watch the sheep coming down the wide lane between the hedgerows.

"Hello, Tank! Hello, Tom Cason!" Jamie called to the two boys bringing in the sheep.

The boys were too busy to answer him. Tank was in front. He had gone ahead to let down the bars into a pasture. Tom and a dog were driving the flock of sheep.

"Look out, Tank!" Tom yelled. "Watch that ram!"

The ram that led the flock had found the opening into the stableyard. Heavy horns curled on his head, and the ram was big and fierce. He wanted to lead the sheep away from the boys and the dog.

Jamie looked around. Tofts had not come out of the stable. There was no one to stop the ram.

"Get back there!" Jamie yelled at the ram. He took a few steps forward and waved his arms. "Whoop! Whoop!" he shouted.

The ram had come inside the stableyard. When Jamie yelled, the ram stopped to glare at

16

the boy out of wicked little eyes. The ram stamped his front feet on the muddy ground, to show that he was angry.

For the first time at Westbrook Place, Jamie saw something going wrong. The ram should not be in the stableyard. Jamie had to drive the ram out.

"If I had a stick, I could drive him out," Jamie thought. He looked at the ground. There was a big stick! He ran to pick it up.

The ram was starting toward the boy. His head was down. He was ready to butt anyone who got in his way.

Jamie stepped to one side and began to run also. Maybe he could turn the ram and drive him back. He waved his stick. "Whoop!" he cried. "Get back! Whoo———sh!"

Jamie had not noticed the big puddle of mud. As he flourished his stick, Jamie's feet slipped out from under him. He fell with a splash right in the middle of the mud.

The yelling boy, the waving stick, and the sudden splash scared the ram. The ram stopped to look. As Jamie pulled himself up out of the mud, the ram turned and ran back into the lane.

"Thank you, Master Jamie," Tom Cason called. "You headed him off for good!" The sheep, the dog, and the boys all moved after the ram to the pasture.

Jamie looked at his muddy clothes. There was

18

a big hole in one of the long stockings Nannie had knit for him. Both stockings were wet through, and one shoe had come off. He fished it out of the mud and went slowly toward the house.

"Now Nannie will fuss," he thought. "She'll say I am not a farm boy, and I shouldn't try to herd the sheep. She'll tell Lady Mother I've been naughty."

Jamie was worried. His sister Fanny was a year older. She would help him. When they were naughty, Fanny could often make Nannie laugh till she forgot to be cross. He would tell Fanny first about the mud and the ram and Sandy and the puppies.

"That big ram didn't scare me a bit," he told himself proudly.

A Lesson in Manners

JAMIE saw no one as he climbed the stairs to the third-floor nursery. He paused at the head of the steps to listen. There was only one sound. The wood in the grate fire burned with a crackle and a hiss. The far side of the room glowed from the light of the fire.

Jamie drew his shoulders back and marched in, like a soldier.

"Fanny," he began, "Tammie's puppies——"

But Fanny wasn't in the room. Only his ten-year-old sister Molly was there. Bent over her embroidery frame that stood in front of her, she sat by the fire. She jumped as her brother spoke.

20

"Ouch!" Molly cried. "Jamie, you bad boy, you scared me——" She popped a needle-pricked finger into her mouth and stared at her brother.

Jamie frowned. Molly would be no help with Nannie. Where was Fanny?

"Whee-e-e!" Molly exclaimed after a second. "Wait till Nannie sees you!"

"I had to help Tom and Tank drive the sheep to the pasture," Jamie said loudly in self-defense.

"Looks as if the sheep drove you," Molly said. She giggled at her own joke.

Jamie went toward the fire, and Molly shifted her embroidery frame. "Watch out!" she cried. "You'll get my sampler muddy."

Nurse Middlecase opened the door between her little bedroom and the big nursery.

"Jamie!" she exclaimed. "What's happened? Are you hurt?"

Jamie squared his shoulders again. "The ram

tried to come into the stableyard," he explained, "and I had to stop him and——"

"The ram knocked you down! Did he hurt you? Where?" Nannie was worried.

"No, Nannie, he didn't. I had a stick, and I made him go back even though I was in the mud. Tom Cason said I did. And I wasn't scared," he boasted.

"Tsk! Tsk!" Nannie clucked. "Jamie, you do get into trouble, but you were a brave laddie to face that ram. Take those muddy clothes off. You're wet all through, and you'll have to have a bath right now."

Nannie bustled about. "There's plenty of hot water in the kettle on the crane," she said. "It would do us all good to have a cup of hot milk before supper." She shoveled hot coals into a heavy iron pan that stood on the hearth and brought milk from the pantry in the hall.

A few minutes later Fanny ran down the hall.

"Is Jamie back?" she called even before she reached the door.

"Oh, Jamie, did you see the puppies? How many——" She saw the muddy clothes in a heap on the floor. "What happened? Did Tammie——"

Jamie tried to pull away from Nannie. "Fanny, they're the prettiest puppies you ever saw. One is all white and——"

"Don't jump about so, Jamie." Nannie had wrapped a heavy towel around his lean body. She rubbed him briskly on head, face, arms, back, and legs.

Molly stood up. "Nannie," she said, "it's getting dark. I'm going to light the candles."

"It's my turn," declared Fanny. She ran to climb up on the wooden settle close to the hearth. She pulled a tightly rolled length of paper from the handful of spills in a copper mug on the mantel.

The slow-moving Molly caught her as she climbed down. Molly grabbed for the twisted paper, but Fanny held it as far away as her arm could stretch.

With a sudden jerk, Fanny twisted out of Molly's grasp. Fanny knelt down to light the spill at the fire. Molly caught Fanny's hand again.

"Molly! Fanny!" Nurse Middlecase seized

each little girl by an arm. She pulled them back from the hearth. She took the unlighted taper from Fanny.

Then Nannie slapped each girl sharply. "Such behavior!" she scolded. "I don't know what Lady Oglethorpe would say if she saw you. Jamie is so clumsy he falls into a mud puddle. Now you girls start scuffling. You all act like country bumpkins!"

She picked up the muddy clothes and the basin of water. "Jamie, put on those clean clothes. Quick, now."

She left the room. A few minutes later she was back.

"Stop sniffling," she ordered. "You children aren't bumpkins. You aren't even ordinary children. Your father was an officer in the King's army. Your mother is a lady and a friend of Queen Anne herself."

Jamie and the two girls were very quiet.

Nannie studied them a minute. "We will have a lesson in court manners," she said. "Jamie, put on that plumed hat."

Jamie ran to get the hat from its peg on the wall. The plumed hat had belonged to his father.

"Now," Nannie went on, "the three of you go to the door and walk in as ladies and gentlemen should. I am Queen Anne, and you will come in and make your bows to me."

Standing beside his sisters and wearing the grown-up hat, Jamie felt very tall.

Fanny started first. She walked slowly and gracefully into the room. Molly was not to be outdone. She stepped slightly ahead. As the older sister, that was her place. Jamie followed.

A few feet from the Queen the girls stopped. Each put her right foot forward and bent her knee until it almost touched the floor. Their heads were bent and their finger tips held their long skirts out wide.

26

Jamie took off his hat. He put one foot forward. He bent both knees, and he bowed his
head. With his right hand he swung the hat so
that its plume just touched the floor.

"Greetings, my subjects," Queen Nannie said. "You may rise." The children stood erect. Carefully Jamie put his hat under his arm.

"Sir James," Nannie said to Jamie, "will you do us the honor of lighting the taper?" She handed him the paper spill. Jamie went to the hearth and set the tip of the taper afire.

"My Lady Mary, will you be so kind as to light the candle on the mantel?" asked Nannie. Molly took the taper Jamie handed her. She stood on tiptoe to light the wax candle.

"My Lady Frances, may I request you to light the candle on the reading stand?" Graciously Molly handed the taper to Fanny; the younger girl lighted the candle by Nannie's chair.

"Bravo! Bravo!" said a voice from the doorway. "Sister Anne and Sister Eleanor are real ladies-in-waiting in France, but they can't make nicer curtsies, I'm sure. And Jamie's bow would do credit to a prince."

28

"Lewis!" the three children exclaimed together. They broke up their game and ran to their big brother.

"Will you tell us a story, Lewis?" Jamie begged. "A story about King Arthur."

"Wait," said Lewis. "I must 'make a leg' to the Queen, too. Your hat, Sir James."

He took the hat from Jamie and put it on. Stepping forward, Lewis bent his legs to make his bow. He swept the hat in a wide circle.

"Your humble servant, Your Majesty," he said to Queen Nannie.

"You are welcome to our court, Sir Lewis," Nannie said. "We will be glad to hear a story."

Lewis laughed. "For old times' sake," he said, "I would like a cup of that hot milk I see on the hearth. Then I'll try to think of a story."

An Old Tale

In a few minutes Lewis was sitting in the big leather chair. Across the hearth from him the three children sat on the high-backed settle. Each of the four sipped hot milk from earthenware mugs. Nannie sat in a low chair near the candle stand.

"Are you dressed to go to Court to see the Queen?" Jamie asked.

"I could wear this to Court," said Lewis, "but not today. Our Lady Mother and I are having guests at dinner in the hall downstairs."

Lewis took a sip from his mug. "Nannie," he said, "I haven't tasted hot milk since I was a lad in your nursery. Remember how Eleanor loved it, and how Anne and Theo hated it?"

"God bless them all," Nurse Middlecase said with a sigh. "And all so far away. Mistress Anne and Mistress Eleanor have been sent off to the Court in France. Mr. Theo thinks himself a fine, grown-up gentleman, but he is mighty young to be in the army way off there in India."

Jamie hardly knew these older sisters and Theo, except for the stories Nannie told about them. "Lewis, tell us about——" Jamie stopped. That wasn't the polite way to ask. "Lewis, will you please tell us the story about how King Arthur got his magic sword?"

"You never get tired of that story, do you?" Lewis said. "Let me tell you about how Arthur used his sword to slay a dragon and free a princess in distress."

"Please tell how Arthur got his sword and *then* about the dragon," pleaded Jamie.

31

Lewis leaned back in his chair. "Many and many a year ago," he began, "it happened that there was no king in England. The king had died, and only a very old man, a magician whose name was Merlin, knew that Arthur was the king's son. Many of the great lords wanted to be king. They were always at war. They fought one another with swords and spears."

"And they had knights," Jamie reminded him.

"Each lord had his own knights," Lewis agreed. "They lived in his castle and fought for him. When a boy grew to be a man, he went to the great lord he most admired and said, 'Let me be your knight.' Then the lord tested him to see if he could use the sword and spear, if he was full of courage, and if he told the truth. When he knew the young man was ready, the lord gave him a sword and made him his knight."

"And he made an oath," Jamie added. "He said:

> " 'I will be brave; I will be bold;
> I will not fear nor heat nor cold;
> I will be true to my liege lord
> While life shall last, so help me God.' "

"That's right," said Lewis. "There were many lords and each had knights, but no one was strong enough, or wise enough, or had enough friends to be king."

"They needed a sign to tell them which lord should be king," Jamie said.

Lewis nodded. "Yes, they did. Merlin was a very wise magician," he went on. "When Arthur was almost grown, Merlin made magic to give them a sign. At Christmastime he called all the lords to London. In a churchyard he showed them a fine steel sword, held fast in a great block of marble.

" 'See that stone and that sword,' Merlin said to them. 'The man who can pull out the sword shall be king of England!' "

Jamie jumped up. "Let's play drawing the sword." He ran to get his wooden sword. "What can be the great stone?" he asked, looking around.

Lady Oglethorpe was standing in the doorway.

"Here's Lady Mother!" Jamie exclaimed.

Everyone jumped up. Jamie and Lewis bowed. The girls and Nannie made curtsies.

"Give me the sword," Lady Oglethorpe said gaily. "I will be your stone." She sat down in Nannie's chair. Nannie went to the settle.

Jamie handed his mother the sword. She held the blade in both hands and put her hands between her knees. Her gray watered-silk skirts looked like marble. The hilt of the sword stood up above them.

"Now, Lewis, you are Merlin," said Lady Oglethorpe. "Call the lords."

Lewis spoke in a deep voice. "Lord Mary, you are noblest of all. Can you take the sword?"

Jamie was excited. He watched the "noblest" fail to draw the sword.

"Lord Frances, you are wisest of all. Try for the sword."

The "wisest" failed too. Fanny turned to smile at Jamie as he waited for his call.

"Lord James, you are bravest of all. Is the sword yours?"

The "bravest" came forward. He grasped the hilt of the sword and tugged hard. The stone did not give.

"Nannie must try, too," Jamie declared.

"Lord Nurse, you are strongest of all. Make your try."

"Great Merlin, the lords have failed. Call the knights," said Lady Oglethorpe.

Merlin summoned them. "Sir Molly, you are pure in heart."

"Sir Fanny, you speak true."

"Sir Jamie, you care for the weak."

"Sir Nannie, you are just to the poor."

The sword hilt stood firm in the marble.

"Merlin," said Lady Oglethorpe, "the lords and knights have all failed. Where can we find a king?"

Lewis spoke in Merlin's deep voice. "No knight has been found worthy to be king. Let the young men who are not yet knights try."

This was the really exciting part. Only Arthur could draw the sword. He was brave and strong and wise and good. Which one would be Arthur?

"Everyone get in line," said Jamie, "and we will take turns."

Molly tried. Fanny tried. Jamie felt the hilt firm in his grasp. He pulled. The sword slipped out so easily that the hand holding it leaped above Jamie's head.

"Jamie is Arthur! Jamie is King Arthur!" cried Fanny.

"Long live King Arthur!" said Lady Oglethorpe and Lewis and Molly and Nannie.

Jamie hesitated, saying the words in his mind before he spoke. "Sir Lewis, will you now recount a tale of your adventures? Have you slain a dragon?"

Just then a tall, brown-faced girl came into the room. She carried a big tray.

Lady Oglethorpe stood up. "No more tales

tonight, my pets," she said. "Here's Polly Cason with your supper." She bent to kiss each one. "Sleep well and dream of adventure."

Jamie kissed his mother. "Good night, my Lady Mother." He turned to Lewis. "Thank you for the story. Will you tell another tomorrow?"

"I must ride to London tomorrow," Lewis answered, "but I will be back for Christmas. When I return, we'll have a tale of adventure every day. Good night."

Later, as Nannie tucked him into bed, Jamie said, "Please tell about seeing King Arthur's big table."

Nannie pulled a stool beside the bed and sat down.

"When I was just a girl," she said, "my father had a farm not far from the city of Winchester. Once, when he went there to sell our eggs and butter at the market, he took all of us children with him. We had honey cakes and cider for lunch, I remember.

"After we ate we walked over a bridge and up a hill to King Arthur's castle. The castle was almost in ruins, but the stone walls of the Great Hall are still standing."

"And it's bigger than our hall downstairs?" Jamie asked.

"Oh me, yes. Our hall is a hall in a manor house. That hall was the Great Hall in the castle of the King. The big table wasn't standing on the floor, as you would expect. There's only the great round top left, and it hangs on the wall at one end of the room. That table was so big that twenty men could sit around it. Above it someone has painted a picture of King Arthur, and the name of a knight is painted at each place around the table.

"The knights would ride away to have adventures, and then they would come home to tell

King Arthur and the other knights the stories. That big table is the reason they were called King Arthur's Knights of the Round Table."

"Nannie, I wish I could be a real Knight of the Round Table."

She patted his arm. "You can be just as fine a man as any one of them, Jamie lad," she said. "Now go to sleep."

Jamie's Orange Trees

Lady Oglethorpe and Lewis were often away from Westbrook Place. At other times they had important visitors. Sometimes Jamie and the girls were dressed up and sent downstairs to make their bows to the guests.

Nannie always sent them down with an old saying, "Remember, 'children should be seen and not heard.'"

One day in the spring Lewis came to say good-by. He wore a fine uniform with gold braid. He had a hat with a plume. There was a sword at his side.

"Are you a knight?" Jamie asked.

"No," Lewis answered seriously. "I am not a knight in a story. I am a soldier, like our father. He was an officer in the army of King James II, and now I am an officer in Queen Anne's army."

"I'd like to be a soldier and go with you, Lewis," Jamie begged.

"Someday you'll be a soldier and fight for your country," Lewis told him, "but our Lady Mother needs you here now."

Lewis' horse, Scimitar, stood saddled at the front of the house. Jamie ran beside him all the way to the gates at the end of the driveway.

"Good-by, Lewis," he called, as long as his brother could hear him.

Days at Westbrook Place were never long enough for Jamie. At home there were lessons in French, writing, and dancing. Jamie had lessons in Latin and arithmetic, too. For these two subjects he went to Mr. Purley. He was the curate of the church of St. Peter and St. Paul.

Mr. Purley lived just behind the church on the edge of the village of Godalming. It was the town nearest to Westbrook Place.

Most afternoons Nannie took the girls for a walk. Sometimes Jamie went with them. They would climb the bluff that was some distance back of the house, or they would cross West Brook on the narrow footbridge to go to the market in Godalming.

Almost every day Jamie rode Sandy. He rode alone over the farm. Old Toft's son, Daniel, or Tom or Tank went with him along the dirt roads that led to villages near by.

Jamie loved best to explore the farm. In the spring he went first to the sheepfold to see if new lambs had been born in the night. Sometimes a ewe would not feed her baby. Jamie helped Tank make the lamb suck milk through a rag.

Men spaded the garden. "Will you plant seeds today?" Jamie asked Cason, the gardener.

"Nay, Master Jamie. We must spade it again in a few weeks. Then we rake it fine before we put in the seeds."

"I'll be back," Jamie promised.

He ran along the creek to the mill.

The heavy millstones made so much noise that the miller did not try to shout a greeting to Jamie. Jamie would not have been able to hear, and the miller waved one hand instead.

Nearer to the house than the farm buildings was the bakehouse. Jamie could always get a slice of fresh bread from the girls working there. Close to the bakehouse were the dairy and the cheesehouse. In another building women spun and wove the thread made from sheep's wool.

Jamie saw hay cut and stored in barns. He saw colts trained and sheep sheared. He watched the men repair thatched roofs on the cottages. Winter and spring, summer and fall, Jamie learned about all the work on a farm.

One spring day Jamie rode Sandy up the drive-way. A coach with two fine horses stood in front of the house. A coachman sat on his high seat, and a footman was near by.

Lady Oglethorpe came out the front door. A gentleman walked with her.

"Jamie," Lady Oglethorpe called, "come here."

Jamie slid down from the saddle. "Stable, Sandy," he said and stopped to watch the horse go on.

"My lord," Lady Oglethorpe said, "this is my son James, of whom I've told you. James, Lord Carew is an old friend of the family. He came to see you."

Jamie made his bow. Lord Carew tapped him on the shoulder with his cane. "A well-grown lad," he said.

"And with a well-grown curiosity, my lord." Lady Oglethorpe laughed. "Not a sheep gets sheared nor a field planted but Jamie must be there."

Lord Carew was pleased. "It never hurts a gentleman to know how to do work with his hands," he told Jamie, "and it never hurts a practical man to dream of making a better world."

He turned to the coach. "I've brought you a present, James," he said. "How strong are you? Can you carry this box?"

Jamie stepped up. "I am very strong, my lord," he said. "I'm sure I can carry it."

There were two boxes. Each held a small tree with dirt about its roots. Jamie had never seen plants with leaves like these. "What are they, my lord?" he asked.

"They are young orange trees, James. Do you know where oranges grow?"

"Yes, my lord. In Spain, where the winters are warm."

46

"Right you are, my lad. My grandfather set out the first orange trees in England at our manor, Beddington Hall. It is my dream to make oranges as common as potatoes in England. Figs ripen early at Westbrook Place. Perhaps oranges will do as well here."

Jamie considered. "They will want a sunny spot, won't they?"

"Yes, and a wall to protect them. Is there a place in your garden?"

Lord Carew gave his cane to the footman. He picked up a box and handed it to Jamie. He himself took the second box.

Jamie went first. The box was heavy, but these plants were so important to Lord Carew that he wouldn't let a footman carry them. Jamie was proud that he had been asked to help.

"I know a good place," he said. He led the way to a corner where a brick wall joined the kitchen wing of the house.

"Here, sir," he said. "Wouldn't this place do?"

"But that's Cook's parsley bed," objected Lady Oglethorpe.

"The lad's right," Lord Carew said. "Parsley will grow anywhere. We will plant our orange trees here because this place will protect them from the cold. There are walls to the north and west. There are currant bushes there to the east. No big trees are here to shade the new orange trees."

A boy from the garden dug the holes, but Lord Carew and Jamie planted the trees.

Then Lord Carew tugged gently at the trees to see that they were set firmly in the earth.

"That is fine," he said to Jamie. "Keep them watered and cover them well in the winter. In a few years you should have oranges to eat."

Jamie gazed at the young trees with special pride. They were his trees. "I will take care of them," he promised.

Men were working in the vegetable garden. Jamie noticed that new leaves were showing in the potato beds.

"Would you come see our potato beds, my lord?" he asked. "Mr. Purley says there were no potatoes at all in England till Sir Walter Raleigh brought the plants from America."

"That's right," Lord Carew agreed. "Sir Walter had many dreams to make England greater. He brought plants from the New World. He was the first to try to send English colonists to live in America."

"Mr. Purley told me about that too, sir," Jamie said. "He said the Spaniards and the French were trying to keep all of America for themselves, but Sir Walter and Sir Francis Drake wouldn't let them."

"Indeed no," said Lord Carew. "Does Mr. Purley teach you history also?"

"No, my lord, but if I've studied my lessons we

have time to talk. Sometimes he lets me read letters from his brother in Virginia."

"Remember all you learn about America, James," advised Lord Carew. "As you grow older you will realize just how important the American colonies and trade with the New World are to England."

When Jamie opened his books that night he found it hard to study. There were so many things to do in the world. Raleigh had brought the potato plants from America and now everyone in England ate potatoes. Lord Carew was trying to grow oranges here, so there would be plenty for all. Perhaps there were other plants, and animals, that could make a better life for everyone in England. Could he go to America, maybe all around the world, to find them?

But he wanted to be a soldier like Lewis and Theo and his father. That was a big job, too.

Something in the Wood

ONE MORNING in the fall before Jamie was ten, he found Mr. Purley waiting in front of the church.

"James," he said, "old Mr. Stedman is ill. He has sent for me to come see him at once. I did not have time to send a boy to Westbrook Place to tell you not to come today."

"I don't mind, sir," Jamie assured him. "I'll be back tomorrow. Good-by."

Jamie considered. He had ridden Sandy today, so he could have a fast run after his lessons.

Now he had a whole morning to himself! He must do something special.

A few days earlier he had been looking at maps in a bookstall in Godalming. An old gentleman had stopped to look, too. "Do you know what land this map shows?" the gentleman had asked.

"Yes, sir. This map shows the coast line of America. Here is Jamestown in Virginia. Jamestown is the town the English colonists built."

"Right you are, my lad. It is good to see a boy interested in maps. What is your name?"

"James Oglethorpe, sir, of Westbrook Place."

"I am William Elliott of Busbridge Hall," the man said. "I knew your father, Sir Theophilus. He was Member of Parliament from this district and so was your brother Lewis."

Jamie knew that Parliament was a group of men who met in London to make laws for the whole country. To be a member was a great honor, of course, but that was not the most important fact about his father and brother. He told Mr. Elliott, "They were both soldiers, too."

"Fine men," said Mr. Elliott. "I was sorry to hear that Lewis was killed on the battlefield."

Jamie said proudly, "The Duke of Marlborough wrote my Lady Mother that Lewis was a hero."

"I am sure he was," Mr. Elliott agreed. "As a young lad Lewis was very brave."

"Yes, sir," Jamie said. "He was as brave as a knight of King Arthur's Round Table."

"So you know those fine tales of our old heroes?" Mr. Elliott was interested.

"Lewis used to tell them to me."

"If you like stories about heroes' adventures, you must come to see me someday at Busbridge Hall," Mr. Elliott said. "My grandfather sailed with Sir Francis Drake. I can tell you about the voyage they made around the world."

"Oh, thank you, sir. I'd like to come," Jamie had answered.

Should he go to Busbridge Hall today? He

knew the road. No, Mr. Purley said a gentleman always wrote a note before he paid a call. Anyway it was too fine an afternoon to spend indoors.

"I know," Jamie decided. "I'll ride through Ockford Wood. Tom and Tank are scared of the wood because they think a ghost lives there. But I'm not afraid."

He looked down at the red-leather sheath that hung from his belt. The sheath held a sharp-bladed knife. His brother Theophilus had just come home from India and had brought it to him. He had wanted to show the knife to Mr. Purley.

A knife was no good if one did see a ghost, of course, but Jamie was glad he had a weapon.

He walked Sandy across West Brook and turned left, away from his home.

At first the road was sunny and open, and Sandy trotted briskly. After he turned into the wood, the little-used road was muddy in the

heavy shade. Trees grew close. Low-hanging
limbs and bushes reached almost across the road.

For a while Jamie could hear West Brook gur-
gling over rocks. Then everything grew quiet.
The sun must be hidden by sudden clouds to
make it so dark.

Jamie began to feel very lonely. Maybe he

shouldn't have come by himself. He wished Tammie were with him.

Sandy seemed restless, too. The muscles on his shoulders quivered.

There was a sudden crash in the woods. Had a tree fallen? Sandy snorted and jerked his head.

"Quiet, boy, it's nothing." Jamie patted the horse's neck and rode on.

He tried to see into the woods. There seemed to be no opening between the tree trunks. Even the road turned so often there was no clear view ahead or behind.

"Yap! Yap! Yap!" The barks were sharp and loud, but they were not close. There was no other sound.

Sandy threw up his head and was ready to turn for home.

Jamie's hand was firm on the rein. "On, Sandy." In the stillness his voice sounded loud to his own ears.

Tom Cason had said once, "Maybe it's not a ghost, but something funny lives in Ockford Wood."

Tank had answered, "It *is* a ghost. I know it is. If I heard dogs going 'Yap! Yap!'—quick and sharp-like—I'd get out of there in a hurry."

Jamie gazed at the dark trees. Was an animal crouching on that tree limb? Ahead, where the road turned, what was that dark lump?

"Yap! Yap! Yap!" The three barks were closer now. They might be wild dogs, or they might be ghost dogs running with a ghost hunter. Nannie had never seen a ghost, but she said her father had. Tofts said there were so many things men did not know that no one could be sure there were no ghosts.

Jamie shivered. He wanted to go fast. He kicked Sandy so hard the little roan lurched sideways. One hind leg slipped in the mud, and he almost went down. Jamie felt himself sliding backward in the saddle. He clutched Sandy's mane and held tight.

Sandy was startled. He reared up.

"He sees the ghost," Jamie thought. Then he told himself sternly, "There is no ghost in this wood. That was just a stump at the turn."

His heart was beating fast. He was glad the trees were thinning out. He could see sunlight ahead.

"Giddap, Sandy!"

The horse broke into a trot. Mud splashed in all directions. For several minutes Jamie rode hard to put the dark wood behind him. Then he slowed Sandy to a walk and looked around.

The Frightened Dog

Soon Jamie passed what must have been a stone quarry. On the far side stood a one-room cottage with roof of thatched straw. Jamie did not know who lived there. He had never seen a poorer-looking house. The shutters hung crookedly, and the roof needed new thatch.

Two boys were dragging something along the road. Jamie stopped to see what they were doing.

The boys stopped, too. Jamie saw that they had a small dog. A cord was tied tightly around his neck. The frightened dog lay on the ground and whimpered.

"You mean boys!" Jamie yelled. "You're chok-
ing that dog. Turn him loose!"

"He's our dog," one of the boys muttered.
"We'll lead him if we want to!"

Jamie slid down from Sandy's back. "Stand,
Sandy," he ordered. He walked toward them.
The boys cowered back. They jerked at the cord
to pull the dog closer to them.

It made Jamie angry to see how much the dog
was suffering. "Take that cord off the dog's
neck," he ordered.

"I won't if I don't want to," the older boy said.
He stuck out his underlip and scowled at Jamie.

"Turn him loose," said Jamie, "or I will."

The smaller boy grabbed up the dog. He
clutched the animal in his arms. "Fight him,
Buss," he said. "Scratch his eyes out!"

Jamie reached for the dog. The boy called
Buss leaped at Jamie. His thin fingers were
stretched out like claws.

Jamie caught Buss by one arm, but the boy pulled loose. He was strong and wiry, and he was taller than Jamie. He clawed at Jamie's face and grabbed his coat. Jamie stepped back and spun around.

The boy lost his hold but came at Jamie again, fingers bent.

Jamie caught the boy's arms and held him tight. Buss twisted and pulled, trying to scratch.

"I'll teach you to hurt a dog!" Jamie shook the boy hard.

Buss's dirty shirt ripped. Through the long torn place Jamie saw a skinny chest and shoulder. The boy was so thin every rib showed. Jamie let go of him. The boy fell to the ground.

"See here," Jamie said in a quieter voice, "I don't want to fight. Can't you see you're hurting your dog? Let me untie the cord. Then we'll make a proper leash to lead him by."

The smaller boy snarled, "Go 'way. He's our

dog! You can't touch him!" The small boy's skinny hands held the dog so tightly he whimpered again and tried to squirm away.

Jamie looked from the boy on the ground to the boy with the dog. All three were terribly thin. He felt as sorry for the boys as he did for the dog.

"Did you ever ride a horse?" he asked them.

The boys stared at him. Jamie waited for an answer. Finally the little one said, "Course not! We got no horse! But we got a dog!"

Jamie smiled. "If you'll let me untie that cord, I'll let you ride Sandy."

The four black eyes were unfriendly. The boys did not trust this stranger who might take their one pet away from them.

"You untie it, then," Jamie suggested. "I won't touch your dog. Then you can ride."

The boys looked at each other. Finally the little boy's fingers reached for the cord. The knot was too tight to untie.

Jamie pulled his new knife out of its sheath. The blade glistened in the light. Jamie had not yet let anyone other than himself use the knife, but now he offered it to the bigger boy.

"Here, Buss," he said slowly, "you cut the string."

Even then Buss hesitated. Slowly he took the knife. His eyes never left Jamie until his hand touched the dog.

"Yipe," the dog yelped as the knife blade slipped between his neck and the string.

When the string was cut, Buss handed the knife back to Jamie. He did not say a word.

"Now," Jamie said, "who wants the first ride?"

"Let Buss," said the smaller boy.

Jamie gave Buss a shove to help him climb on Sandy's back. The boy was scared to find himself so high above the ground. "I'll fall off," he gasped.

"No, you won't," Jamie assured him. "I'll lead

Sandy." He walked Sandy up the road and back again.

Buss slipped down. "It's grand, Little Un," he said. "You'll like it."

Little Un climbed up with Jamie's help. He too was scared, but he didn't say a word. Up the road and back again Jamie led the horse.

Little Un slid down without a word. He looked at Buss and then at Jamie with shining eyes.

"Now," said Jamie, "let's make a leash."

He needed a strap. He looked at the horse's bridle and then at his own belt. Quickly he took off the belt. With the point of his knife he made a hole about nine inches from the buckle.

While Little Un held the dog, Jamie put the belt around the dog's neck and fastened the buckle. He handed the end of the strap to Buss.

"Now you can lead your dog without hurting him," he said. "He is a nice dog."

Little Un looked up shyly. "Thank you," he said, "and thank you for the ride."

Jamie put his foot in the stirrup and mounted Sandy. "Good-by," he called.

Both boys stood in the road and watched Jamie out of sight.

"Those poor boys," Jamie thought. "They love that dog."

He remembered the skinny bodies, the ragged clothes, and the condition of the thatch on the cottage roof.

"I wonder who owns this land?" he thought. "We would never let anyone at Westbrook Place live like that. I can ask Nannie for some clothes for them and tell Tofts to send some food."

Somehow on the way home the wood did not seem so dark or the road so long. Jamie didn't once think about a ghost.

Country and Town

THERE WAS very little Jamie could do for the poor family near the quarry. "Poor country folk aren't like poor city folk," Nannie declared. "Maybe country folk are poor and maybe shiftless and maybe they will steal, but they are proud, too. They won't like it if you give them things as though you were sorry for them."

Tofts was doubtful also about sending food to people who lived on someone else's land. "I'll go by and see if there's anything we can do," was all he would promise Jamie.

When cold weather came, Nannie made up a bundle of clothes. "You just ride over and leave this at the edge of the wood," she told Jamie. "They'll find it. What they find, they'll use," she added grimly.

Later Jamie rode all the way to the quarry again. The boys came out of the cottage to meet him. They were wearing the clothes, but not a word was said about the bundle.

"Would you like to ride Sandy again?" he asked after he had greeted them.

Buss and Little Un looked at each other and then back at Jamie. They grinned and ducked their heads shyly.

Buss was boosted up. He clutched the saddle, but Jamie made him take the reins. "Sandy won't throw you off," he assured Buss. "I'll run beside you and turn him around."

Little Un was more venturesome. As soon as he was in the saddle, he grabbed the reins and clucked to Sandy. A little later he used his heels and made the horse trot.

Jamie laughed. "You'll be a good horseman, Little Un."

As Jamie started away he looked back at the house. New straw had been added, and the thatch looked rainproof now. "Tofts must have sent that straw," he thought, "and the boys didn't look so hungry."

The next day Jamie wrote the following letter:

Dear Mr. Elliott,

May I call at Busbridge Hall on Tuesday afternoon?

Your humble servant,
James Edward Oglethorpe

He asked young Daniel Tofts to take the note. An hour later Daniel was back with the reply:

My dear James,

I will be most happy to see you.

Your obedient servant,
William Elliott

Tuesday afternoon Jamie rode over to Busbridge Hall.

"Come into the library, James," Mr. Elliott said. "You would like to see my globe first, I am sure."

"Yes, sir. I've never seen a globe."

Jamie was astonished that this ball could show all the countries and oceans. Here, on a small scale, was the whole great round world.

"Find the countries you know, James," Mr. Elliott suggested. "Then I'll show you the route Sir Francis Drake took when he sailed his ship around the world."

"Here's England." Jamie pointed. How tiny it was! France was just a small part of Europe. The blue for the oceans took so much more space than the colors of the countries. Look at America! The land stretched almost all the way from north to south. Of course! There were two Americas and then another ocean.

"Is this the way to India, sir?" he asked.

"It's one way. It's the way Drake sailed." Mr. Elliott took up a pointer and traced the route as he talked of the places: England, across the Atlantic Ocean to North America, down the east coast of South America and all the way up the west coast, across the Pacific Ocean to the islands in the South Seas, then to India, down south again, around the tip of Africa into the Atlantic Ocean, and home again.

Jamie drew a deep breath. "What a long voyage," he said.

"It took three years." Mr. Elliott took a book from the shelves. "Here is Captain John Smith's *Generall Historie of Virginia, New England, and the Summer Isles,*" he said. "Smith was another great adventurer. Perhaps you'd like to read this."

Jamie enjoyed Captain Smith's book about colonies in the New World. "I liked all the parts about the Indians," he told Mr. Elliott when he returned the book, "but most of all I liked Captain Smith."

"He was a great man, James," Mr. Elliott agreed. "Like Sir Francis Drake, Captain Smith never was afraid of danger. He never asked his men to stand more hardship than he took on himself. Both Captain Smith and Sir Francis Drake were great heroes."

Mr. Elliott's library was a treasure house to

Jamie. He thought he could never see it all. There were books, maps, Grandfather Elliott's spyglass and sextant and sea clock, the curios from America and foreign islands.

After each visit Mr. Elliott sent him off with, "Come again, James. I have something else to show you."

Lady Oglethorpe asked Jamie, "Why do you go to see Mr. Elliott so often? He is an old man, and you are just a boy."

Jamie protested, "He is my friend. I like to talk with him."

That fall Lady Oglethorpe took her family back to London again. She was very much excited as she told Jamie, Molly, and Fanny about her plans.

"Our town house has been rented for three years," she said, "but now we shall have it again. I was sure things would work out in time and they have. Children, we're almost rich again! Not as we were once, of course, but we shall have new draperies and new carpets. I shall be at home to callers every Tuesday. Molly and Fanny, in a few years you will be old enough to be ladies-in-waiting to the Queen. It's time I began to teach you what your duties will be."

"Oh, Lady Mother, how wonderful!" the girls said happily.

"Jamie," Lady Oglethorpe said, "you shall go to a proper school. My dear boy, you look more like your handsome father every day."

Lady Oglethorpe beamed at her children, and they beamed back at her.

"She is the most beautiful lady in all the world," Jamie thought lovingly.

"Jamie," suggested Lady Oglethorpe, "pull the bell rope and tell Polly to bring tea and cakes. We shall have a party, just the four of us, right now."

After she had poured the tea, Lady Oglethorpe

said, "Did I tell you Anne and Eleanor are coming from France for a long, long visit? Since Theo will be a Member of Parliament, he will be at home, too. It will be wonderful to have my whole family together again!"

At first Jamie thought it was exciting to live in London. The front door of their town house opened directly on the street. People were always passing. His brother Theo and other young gallants strolled along. They all wore bright-colored suits, wide hats with plumes on them, and red-heeled shoes. Fine ladies dressed in silks and furs rode in coaches.

All day long, shop boys wearing wooden clogs clattered over the paving stones. The boys shouted at one another. Sometimes they fought in the street till coachmen had to use whips to drive the boys out of the way.

"Jamie," said Lady Oglethorpe, "you must never leave unless someone is with you."

76

"But, Lady Mother," argued Jamie, "I can run fast."

"No, dear." Lady Oglethorpe was firm. "You might get lost. You've never known boys like these street rogues. They like nothing better than to beat up a boy in good clothes."

Jamie had no one with whom to talk. Theo was seldom at home. His older sisters, Anne and Eleanor, were busy with Molly and Fanny.

"All they ever talk about is a new dress for Fanny and how to comb Molly's hair," Jamie grumbled.

He longed for the boys on the farm, for his horse Sandy, and for his dog Tammie. He missed his visits to Mr. Elliott and to the quarry.

"I'll be glad to start to school," he thought.

Bread and "Coffins"

THE LONDON house was not so large as the manor house at Westbrook Place, but it was more richly furnished. There were more servants, too. All were new except Nurse Middlecase and Polly Cason.

"I like them all except Grubble," Jamie told Nannie.

Grubble was the footman. He opened the door for guests, helped wait on the table, and polished silver.

"I hate Grubble!" Jamie told Nannie angrily a day or so later. "He's mean and he likes to see someone hurt."

"Has he hurt you?" Nannie asked quietly.

"No—and he'd better not. But today he kicked a poor old dog out in the back areaway."

"Did you see him?" Nannie demanded.

"No, I didn't see him do it. I heard the poor dog yelp. I looked out and saw the dog run. It was limping. Grubble stood there, laughed, and rubbed his hands together the way he does."

"Maybe he didn't kick the dog," Nannie suggested. "You know Lady Oglethorpe doesn't allow dogs here."

"You're just saying that, Nannie," James protested. "I don't believe you like Grubble any better than I do. I don't trust him. Do you?"

Nannie didn't answer the question. "I never saw a boy get angry as fast as you do," she said sharply. "You will never be a gentleman till you learn to control that temper."

When Grubble was told to walk with him to school, Jamie fumed to himself, "Why couldn't it have been one of the other servants? I just don't like Grubble."

He walked ahead of Grubble. "If I must have a servant," he thought, "I'll be a gentleman and keep him behind me."

As they passed some small shops, Jamie heard Grubble laughing. He looked around. He thought the footman might try to play some trick on him.

Grubble was rubbing his hands together.

"Ah-h, look-y there, Master Jamie," he said. "Watch that nipper get caught."

A barefoot boy dressed in a ragged gray coat was creeping up to a baker's shop. Some loaves of bread were lying on a shelf outside the window. The boy's hand reached toward one loaf and then drew back.

Grubble darted forward. He grabbed the boy. As Grubble moved, his arm knocked a loaf of bread to the ground.

80

"Caught you, you thief!" Grubble cried. "Mr.
Bell!" he called. "Mr. Bell, here be a thief steal-
ing your bread."

The ragged boy was struggling.

Jamie was angry. He jumped between them
and broke Grubble's hold on the boy. "He didn't
even touch the bread, Grubble!"

The footman quickly seized the boy's arm again. Jamie heard him mutter, "I'll show the young master." Grubble pushed the boy to the door of the shop. "Call the bailiff, Mr. Bell. He will take this scamp to jail right enough."

Mr. Bell came to the door. He was a kind-faced man with white hair that fell to the collar of his coat.

The boy was crying now. "I didn't take nothing," he whined. "I didn't touch nothing."

Jamie felt very sorry for the poor boy. Perhaps he had meant to steal the bread, but his hand had not touched it. He certainly looked hungry.

Grubble laughed. He shook the boy roughly. "There's the very loaf he was taking," he said. "I knocked it right out of his hand."

"Why, you knocked that loaf off the shelf when you grabbed him!" Jamie turned to the baker. "Mr. Bell, the boy didn't touch your bread."

Mr. Bell looked at the three of them. "Let the

lad loose, Mr. Grubble," he said. "I was watching. The young gentleman is right. The boy didn't touch the bread. You knocked it to the ground. You should pay me for it."

Grubble was surprised, but he tried to bluster. "He is a thief!" he shouted. "I know a thief when I see one."

Jamie reached into the leather bag that hung at his belt. It held only the penny his mother had given him that morning. "I will pay you for the bread, Mr. Bell. Will this be enough?"

Grubble shook the boy and then shoved him away. "Guttersnipe! Thief!" he said.

Jamie picked up the bread and brushed the dust off its hard crust.

The boy watched him. "It isn't dirty," he said. "I could eat it." Although he was still afraid of Grubble, he was quick to clutch the bread when Jamie offered it to him. "I'm so hungry," he half sobbed. "My father's too sick to work——"

Grubble was angry. "You'll be late for school, Master Jamie," he said in a spiteful tone. "Come along." He put his hand on Jamie's arm and pulled him away.

Jamie shook off the footman's hand and walked ahead. He turned to look back. Mr. Bell was talking to the boy. Jamie saw them go into the shop together.

Grubble was muttering, "You think you're so fine. Just wait till you get to school. They will lick all that smartness out of you. I've heard about all the birch switches Mr. Stephens wears out on the scholars. Just try to be so fine there! Why, they'll hang you up by the thumbs!"

Grubble knew nothing about schools, Jamie felt sure, but neither did he. Mr. Purley had been kind and had explained lessons to him. Maybe the new teachers—but he would not let Grubble know he was nervous. Jamie squared his shoulders and walked faster.

Mr. Stephens' Grammar School for Boys was not large. Classes were held in an ugly brick building. At one side was an open courtyard with a high fence around it.

Mr. Stephens was the headmaster. He asked Jamie what he had studied. "I'll put you in Form Four," he said. "Mr. Peters is master of that class. If he can give you extra help in Greek, perhaps you can go into Form Three next term."

The first day was not bad at all. Except that there were other boys in the class, lessons were not very different from Jamie's lessons with Mr. Purley.

When the boys went outside for a brief recess, there was an old woman at the gate. She had a big basket filled with meat pies and ginger cookies. The boys called her "Mother Gray." They crowded around her to spend their farthings and pennies.

Jamie stood back and watched. He looked

very much alone among all the other busy boys. One of the boys saw him.

"I say, you're new, aren't you? What's your name?"

"James Oglethorpe."

"I'm Robin Castell," the other boy said. He began to eat his pie, staring at Jamie. "Get your 'coffin' and let's go sit on the fence," he suggested.

Jamie's eyes grew wide. "What?"

Robin held up the pie in his hand. The pie was oblong and shaped rather like a small box. "We call 'em 'coffins.' " He laughed. "They're boxes of pastry filled with meat."

Jamie ran a few steps toward the old woman. He stopped suddenly. He had no money! He had used his spending money for the bread.

He turned back toward Robin. "I don't want one," he started to say. But he did want one!

Robin guessed he had no money. "Here," he

said. "I got two pies. Take one." He shoved a "coffin" toward Jamie.

Jamie put his hands behind his back.

"Take it," Robin urged.

"All right." Jamie reached for the pie. "I'll buy you one tomorrow."

"I say, what's happening there? Must be a fight! Come on!" Robin led the way to a group of boys forming a circle.

But it wasn't a fight. One boy had brought a big top to school. The top worked with a whip and a string. On the hard-packed earth of the schoolyard, the top spun in a wide circle. All the boys wanted to try it.

The owner of the top saw Robin and Jamie. "You're the new boy, aren't you?" he asked Jamie. "I'm Granby. What's your name?"

"Granby talks like a man," Jamie thought. The boy had given his name, just as Jamie's brother Theo introduced his friends.

"I'm Oglethorpe," he said.

"Look, Granby, the top fell over! Isn't it my turn now?"

Granby looked at the speaker. "No, Fenwick, I promised Digby he could have two tries. You're next, then Castell, and then you, Oglethorpe."

In just a few minutes a man came out and rang a big hand bell. It was time for lessons again.

The First Fight

AT RECESS the next day, Jamie ran out to buy a treat for his new friend Castell.

Another boy stopped him. "I'm Baston," he announced gruffly, "and I'm cock of the walk in Form Four. You must do whatever I say. Go buy me a coffin."

Jamie was surprised. He resented the rude command. "I won't," he said.

Baston stepped closer. "You heard me, Ogle-thorpe." He scowled as he looked Jamie over. "You're tall and skinny," he said with a sneer, "but you're probably afraid to fight. Here, Henning, hold my coat. I'll show this jackanapes I mean what I say. There isn't anyone I am afraid to fight."

Other boys ran up. Ready hands took Jamie's coat. Before he knew what was happening he was pushed into the center of a circle of boys.

Baston danced about, moving his fists back and forth. "I'll knock your brains out—if you have any," he threatened.

"Give it to him, Cock!"

"He doesn't know how many beans make five."

"Teach the new boy his manners."

Jamie looked at the circle of faces. The boys wanted to see a fight. Clearly they expected "the cock" to win.

Baston walked up. He hit Jamie on the chest.

Jamie jerked back. The blow had not hurt, but it made him angry. His hands clenched into tight fists. Blindly he struck at the other boy. Baston was alert. He ducked the blows and hit Jamie twice, almost knocking him down.

Jamie regained his balance. His arms blocked the next few blows Baston aimed at him.

"Can't hit me! Can't hit me!" Baston taunted.

Jamie met the dare. His fists flew out wildly. Some of his blows missed but some landed.

Baston backed away and stepped to one side.

In a moment he came back with a hard blow on Jamie's cheek. The blow knocked Jamie sideways. He felt a foot catch his ankle and give a quick jerk. His head hit the ground hard as he fell.

Baston fell on him and grabbed for Jamie's shoulders. Jamie's long arms clutched the other boy.

Jamie was struggling to get on top when a pair of hands took hold of his shoulders and pulled him up. It was Granby who had stopped the fight. Jamie's fists were still clenched.

"Time to stop, Oglethorpe," Granby said. "Here's old Smathers with his bell."

The circle of boys had broken up. They were all heading back into the school building.

"Henning tripped you," Granby told Jamie as they followed. "You'll have to fight again. Baston tries to be a bully, but he isn't mean. His friend Henning is just a sneak. The next fight will be fair. We will see that it is."

"I'll fight him again, whether he's fair or not," grunted Jamie grimly.

Grubble was curious as they walked home. "Looks as if you might have had a fight," he said, grinning.

Jamie did not answer.

"Expect you got too hoity-toity," Grubble went on. "It don't do for a new boy to put on airs."

Jamie strode along the street. "Baston may be a bully, but he can't scare me," he said through clenched teeth.

Grubble was silent, but Jamie felt the man's

hard eyes on him. Just before they reached home, Grubble said quietly, "Master Jamie, I don't expect you learned to fight, down there in the country. If you'll come down to the basement, I'll teach you."

Jamie was surprised. He stopped and looked at the man. Was Grubble trying to trick him?

"Can't have it said my young gentleman can't fight," Grubble said. "We'll show 'em."

Jamie decided to take the risk. "Thank you, Grubble. I'll be down."

Nannie was worried because Jamie had been fighting. She washed the big bump on his head.

"Gentlemen don't fight with their fists," she told him sternly. "Don't you know enough to keep this arm up over your face?" She pulled Jamie's right arm into position. "That way he can't hit your head."

She dipped a cloth in hot water and put it back over the bump.

"Just like a guttersnipe, rolling in the dirt," she grumbled. "If you'd hold his shoulders down, he couldn't roll you over."

"I was tripped——" Jamie began.

"Just got so angry you tripped yourself, most likely." Nannie sniffed. "You can't hit when you're too angry to see."

Later that day Jamie met Grubble in the basement. "Let's start at the beginning, Master Jamie. Put your left foot forward, and your right fist in front of your chin. Stay on the balls of your feet and keep moving. Hold your left fist forward and use it to jab at the stomach or chin. That'll keep the other fellow off balance."

Grubble took the position he had described. He crouched slightly and began to move, bobbing backward and forward and sideways. His left fist flicked out several times toward an imaginary opponent. Then suddenly he shifted his weight and threw his right fist.

"Now let's see you do that," he said.

Jamie got into position. He tried to move around lightly, but his feet kept bumping together. Once when he pulled his right fist back he hit his own chin.

Grubble laughed, half-sneeringly. "You do that and you'll knock yourself out. You have a lot to learn. Watch me. You aim to hit him with your right, see, but you must make him think it's your left that is coming."

Jamie practiced hard. After an hour Grubble said, "You're looking better, Master Jamie. Pity we haven't someone your size. It wouldn't do you any good to hit me, but tonight I'll make a punching bag filled with sand. We can hang it by a rope down here."

"I'll be back," Jamie promised. "I've got to learn to fight."

Grubble grinned. "And I'm the man can teach you how to fight."

96

Jamie lay awake a long time that night. He thought about the fight.

"I'll whip Baston if I have to fight him every day for a year," Jamie vowed.

Nannie was right. You couldn't hit if you were too angry to see. Nannie might not want him to fight, but if he had to fight, she surely did want him to win. And Grubble knew how to fight.

He had friends at school, too. He liked Granby and Robin Castell. Jamie remembered he had not bought that "coffin" for Castell. He must do that tomorrow——

The Second Fight

JAMIE was lucky. It rained for several days and the boys could not play outside. Mother Gray was allowed to come in the hall to sell her wares. Jamie did not forget to buy the "coffin" for Robin.

Every day Baston reminded Jamie, "Tomorrow! Just you wait." But on the one fine day in two weeks Baston was not at school.

The next day he told Jamie, "My father took me to the market fair yesterday. I saw a man fight a bear. I'm going to knock you out just as that man did the bear."

"You can't," Jamie answered stoutly.

One rainy recess period Jamie picked up a book from Mr. Peters' desk. At the top of the first page was a crude, woodcut picture of a man with a bow and arrow.

Jamie showed it to Castell. "Look, Robin," he said, "that's the way men used to shoot before they had guns. Even soldiers in battle fought with bows and arrows."

Robin looked at the woodcut. "I can draw a better picture than that."

He brought his slate and pencil. First he drew a man walking. One arm was poised holding the bow. Then Robin drew a wavy line to show a hillside and some blurred patches for trees and bushes. Down in one corner he drew a rabbit leaping away.

Granby strolled over to the desk.

Jamie knew now that this friend was the eldest son of John Manners, the Duke of Rutland. The boy's name was John Manners, too, and he would someday be the Duke of Rutland. Until then, however, his own title was the Marquess of Granby. Sometimes his best friends called him Jack, but he always signed himself just "Granby."

Granby looked at the picture on Robin's slate. "You've got it all wrong."

Jamie defended Robin. "How do you know, Jack?" he asked. "I've seen Timothy Cason hold his bow just like that."

"Not when he was shooting rabbits," Jack said. "Look! This is the way to hold a bow."

He stood straight with feet apart, head turned to his left. His left hand held the imaginary bow out to his side. His right forefinger flicked as though releasing an arrow. The straightened finger followed the flight the arrow would make.

"Your arrow is aimed too high. It would hit away up here." Granby pointed to Robin's slate. He laughed. "And away would go the rabbit, hoppity-hoppity-hop."

Robin rubbed out the picture. "I'll draw another one."

Mr. Peters' voice rang out sharply. "Gentlemen! It is lesson time. Didn't you hear me come in?"

He reached over and took Robin's slate. He tapped each boy sharply with his cane.

"Back to your places. Oglethorpe, open your Latin book to page 68," he ordered. "Translate the words in the fourth line into English."

Jamie had studied the lesson. He read the words correctly.

"Castell, take the next line."

Poor Robin's mind was still on his picture. He missed two words.

Mr. Peters said, "For the next hour, Castell, you will study in the corner with the dunce's cap on your head."

A red-faced Robin took from Mr. Peters' desk a tall cap. It had the word DUNCE in big letters on the side. He put it on and went to sit on the stool in one corner of the room.

Jamie caught his eye and smiled at him. "Robin likes to draw, but he doesn't like Latin," Jamie thought. "Maybe I can help him tomorrow."

Jamie was beginning to enjoy his lessons with Grubble even though the footman still made fun of him. He liked to punch the bag. Each blow sent a shock running from his fist to his shoulder. He was learning what to do with his fists and his feet.

"Nannie," he said one night, "I think I know why Grubble seems so mean sometimes. He doesn't like to be a footman and have to take orders. He used to be a fighter, but he broke his wrist. He likes to teach me to fight."

Nannie sniffed. "You and that Grubble! A gentleman has no cause to use his fists. I ought to tell Lady Oglethorpe."

Jamie was alarmed. "Please don't, Nannie!" he begged. "She'd try to make me promise not to fight, and I've got to fight Baston."

"Look here, Master Jamie," said Grubble one day, "I'll show you something. You move in this way quick, with your head down, and butt him in the chin so nobody sees you doing it."

"That wouldn't be fair," Jamie protested.

"It's one way to win," answered Grubble, "and you may need it."

"I may need it," Jamie thought, "but I couldn't use it. I'll just have to keep trying till I win fairly."

Then came a clear, cold day.

"This is it, Master Jamie," said Grubble on the way to school. "This is the very day for a fight. I wish I could see it."

At recess Baston was waiting. "Go buy that 'coffin' for me," he ordered.

Jamie looked at him steadily. "I won't," he said clearly.

"You had your chance, Oglethorpe. I'm the cock of this form, and I don't take 'no' from a newcomer."

All the boys were listening. They had been waiting eagerly for this fight. They grabbed the coats Jamie and Baston took off.

"Fair play, Baston," Granby snapped. "Henning, you keep back."

Jamie remembered his lessons. He shifted his

weight on his feet and raised his fists. Jamie knew this time what he must do.

"Look at the jackanapes!" Baston sneered. "He acts as if he could fight." He rushed forward, hitting out strongly with both fists.

Jamie danced backward. He flicked his left fist at Baston's nose. He felt the blow land solidly. A moment later one of Baston's fists drove through Jamie's guard. Jamie's chin hurt.

They began to fight more cautiously. Jamie hit Baston in the stomach, but then he was hit hard on the side of the head.

Baston wiped his face. As he took his hand down, he saw blood on it. "My nose is bleeding," he roared. "You nasty little scamp!" He advanced furiously.

"This is the right moment," Jamie thought. He shifted to one side, set himself, and swung his right fist with all his strength behind it.

The blow landed flush on Baston's chin. His

knees buckled under him. Slowly he fell to the ground.

"That did it," said Granby happily. "He won't bother you again."

"Good show," said Fenwick and some of the others.

"Jamie," Robin cried suddenly, "your lip is bleeding."

Jamie smiled. His lip hurt, but he was too happy to mind the pain. As he turned he met old Smathers with his bell.

The man stared at him. "I'll get some cold water for that lip," he offered.

Jamie looked back. Baston was standing up. "Better get some water for him first," he said. "I'm all right."

Trouble over Oranges

EVEN THOUGH Jamie and Grubble had become good friends, Jamie felt too grown up now to need an escort to school. Many of the boys in his form went out on the streets alone.

Every morning before school Jamie stopped in his mother's bedroom for a short visit. Several times he had asked to go to school alone. His gay, talkative mother would never listen to him.

One day in the spring Jamie could stand it no longer. As he tapped on the door, he thought over his argument.

Fanny opened the door. "Here's Jamie, Lady Mother. May we tell him our plan?"

Anne set her cup of chocolate on a table. "Yes, let's tell him!"

"Good morning, Lady Mother. Good morning, Anne, Fanny, Molly." He "made a leg" to each sister in his best manner.

"Ah, my shining young knight," Lady Oglethorpe greeted him. She gave him a quick kiss. "We hope you will be as excited as we are. Your very next holiday we shall hire a hackney coach to go to see the sights of London."

"We'll climb the stairs of St. Paul's Cathedral and talk in the Whispering Gallery," said Anne.

"And go to a puppet show," Fanny said.

"And to the Tower of London where your hero, Sir Walter Raleigh, was a prisoner," said Lady Oglethorpe.

"And see the Queen's jewels on display," Molly said.

All of them were talking at once. Jamie hardly heard what they said. "Lady Mother," he said at the first pause, "it really isn't necessary for Grubble to take me to school any longer. Please, may I go alone?"

"And we might have time——" Lady Oglethorpe was talking on. She stopped and looked at Jamie. "What is it, dear? Don't you want to go with us?"

"Yes, Lady Mother, I would like to, but my question is important. Digby and Castell come to school by themselves and ——"

Anne put her arm around Jamie. "Why not let him go alone, Lady Mother?" she asked. "He's an Oglethorpe, and no Oglethorpe likes to be babied."

"But Jamie is——" Lady Oglethorpe stopped. She had almost said "my baby." She looked hard at her son. "Yes, you are growing up." She smiled. "Send Grubble to me. I need him this morning, anyway."

It was much more interesting to be on the

street in the early morning all by himself. It was a sunny day and many people were out.

Maids were scrubbing the front steps of the houses. They sang at their work. Men and boys carried big bundles on their heads or in their arms. "Make way! Make way!" they yelled.

Apprentice boys in front of the shops called, "What do you lack? Come buy! Come buy!"

"Here are chestnuts! Hot roasted chestnuts!"

"Fresh fish! Fresh fish!"

"Buy my ribbons. Red ribbons! Green ribbons! Come buy!"

The ribbon rosettes looked gay. Many young men were wearing them now, on their sleeves or pinned on their coats. Granby always wore one. Jamie's brother Theo usually wore several.

Jamie stopped. "How much are they?"

"A shilling each, young master."

Jamie looked in his moneybag. He had two shillings and threepence. He took out the shil-

110

lings. "I want two red ones," he said. The woman handed him the rosettes, and Jamie went on.

Signs painted in bright colors hung above every door. One showed a tiny tree hung with bright yellow oranges. Under the sign boys were yelling, "Oranges! Here are your oranges! Oranges just in from Spain!"

Jamie stopped. They would be good with the cakes Mother Gray sold at the school. "I'll buy two," he told an apprentice.

He took a penny from the bag at his belt and held it out.

"Here you be! Fine oranges! Come buy oranges!"

Jamie thought how good the fruit would taste. He had another penny. If he bought more, he could share with Robin and Granby and Digby.

He turned back to the fruitseller. Just then two boys bumped into him. One hit his arm hard, and Jamie's oranges flew into the air.

"Watch out!" Jamie cried.

He stooped to pick up the fruit, but one of the boys gave him a shove. He fell on the cobblestones.

Each boy grabbed up an orange. They ran away as fast as they could go.

Jamie jumped up and started after them.

The boys stopped at a safe distance. "Yah! Yah! Can't catch me! Yah! Yah!" they yelled at Jamie.

Jamie stopped. He was angry, but he knew it would do no good to try to catch them. "What a mean trick!" he muttered.

If Grubble had been with him, the boys wouldn't have dared steal from him. "I won't let anyone play that trick on me again," Jamie declared to himself. "Well, they can have those. I'll buy some more."

As he hurried back to the fruitseller, he thought about the two boys. They must have been very hungry to steal food. Grubble had told him about the hard life of the London street boys.

Jamie held out his last penny to the fruitseller's apprentice. "Two oranges. Quick!"

Bells began to ring in all the church steeples. "Seven o'clock! Seven o'clock!" they called. He would have to run all the way to school.

Jamie grabbed his oranges and started to run. He watched for the other boys who might try to trick him. He did not notice that a door opened suddenly, and a man came out of a coffeehouse in a hurry.

Jamie jumped to get out of the way. He almost stumbled over a beggar woman. She was crouching against the building. "A farthing, your honor," she whined at everyone who passed. She pulled at Jamie's jacket.

Jamie looked down. The old woman had a bright-eyed child wrapped in her shawl.

"A farthing, kind lad, a farthing," she begged.

The child saw the bright-colored oranges and reached out toward them. Jamie jerked away and ran a few steps. Then he came back.

"Here's an orange for the baby," he said. He thrust it into the child's little hand.

The bells stopped ringing just as he reached school.

At recess Jamie could not buy anything from Mother Gray, but Robin Castell shared his gin-

gerbread with Jamie, in return for half of the orange.

After they had eaten, Jamie gave Robin one of the red ribbon rosettes he had bought. "I'll tie yours on, Robin," he said. "Then you tie this one around my arm."

Robin was much pleased. He held his decorated arm out stiffly, to show off the rosette. "Aren't we handsome!" he said proudly.

"I'm glad Grubble won't be waiting for me," Jamie thought at the end of the day. "I can take care of myself. Those street boys won't trick me again."

A tall, thin boy was waiting outside Mr. Bell's bakeshop. "Master Jamie," he said.

Jamie glanced at him. He did not feel very friendly to any boy on the streets of London that day. He scowled.

"Master Jamie," said the boy again, "don't you know me?"

"No, I don't," Jamie answered.

"Mr. Bell lets me work here now," the boy went on. "I see you go by every day, but I'm afraid of Mr. Grubble."

It was the boy who had been so hungry!

"Oh, I didn't recognize you," said Jamie.

"I'm Jeremy Tickle. I didn't say thank you for that loaf of bread," the boy said shyly. "Mr. Bell gave me something to eat so I could take the bread home."

A man in a black suit came out of the shop. He put his hands on the boy's shoulder. "Good-by, Jeremy," he said. "Tell thy father I will see him soon. Maybe we can find a way to send him to the colony."

"Thank you, Mr. Penn," Jeremy said.

So this was the gentleman who had started a colony for Quakers in the New World! Jamie had heard of Mr. Penn's colony. It was called Pennsylvania.

Mr. Penn looked at Jamie. He smiled. "Isn't thee the lad that gave a poor child an orange this morning?" he asked. "I saw thee run away."

"Oh, I wasn't running away, sir," Jamie told him. "I was late for school."

Jamie gazed at Mr. Penn. He looked and talked like a gentleman, but he was not dressed like one. His suit was black wool, not colored silk. He did not wear a fur-lined cloak, as Theo and his friends did.

"It was a kind deed," Mr. Penn said. "What is thy name, lad?"

"James Oglethorpe, sir."

"Indeed! Was thy father Theophilus Oglethorpe?"

"Yes, sir."

"I knew him. Give Lady Oglethorpe my greetings. Tell her William Penn compliments her on having a fine son."

The Debtors' Prison

ONE AFTERNOON, some weeks later, Jamie was walking home alone. He heard a shout. He glanced across the street and saw Jeremy Tickle. The baker's helper was carrying a sack of flour. Jamie crossed over to walk with him.

"Oh, there's Mr. Penn!" Jeremy exclaimed suddenly.

Sure enough, the Quaker gentleman was coming toward them. There were two men with him, one on each side. They wore dirty red coats, yet they did not look like soldiers. They were certainly not gentlemen, either.

"Good day, Mr. Penn," said Jeremy.

Mr. Penn had not noticed the boys. His face wore a worried frown, but he smiled when he recognized Jeremy. "Good day, lad," he said.

One of his companions put a hand on Mr. Penn's arm. "Come along, sir."

"Why did he do that?" Jamie asked in surprise as the three went on.

"They must have arrested Mr. Penn," Jeremy cried. He began to hurry toward the bakeshop as fast as he could go.

Mr. Bell was standing at the door. He also looked worried. "Jeremy!" he shouted. "Make haste!"

He came to meet the boys. "I'll take the flour," he said. "Mr. Penn just passed with two of the bailiff's men. They're taking him to prison. You must follow, Jeremy, to see which prison."

"We just met them," Jamie said. "I'll go with you, Jeremy."

The two boys set out at a run. They followed

the men a long way. Jamie knew many of the streets of London now, but soon they were in a poor part of the city he had never seen. The streets were narrow and dark. They smelled bad, too. Many people seemed to live here in the drab, ugly old houses. Ragged children fought or played in the streets.

Jeremy said, "They're taking Mr. Penn to the Fleet Street Prison. That's where they take people who can't pay their debts."

"But Mr. Penn is a gentleman," Jamie objected.

"He gives away all his money," Jeremy explained. "Sometimes he even pays passage for poor families like mine to go to his colony in America."

Jamie watched the three men go through the big iron gates of the prison.

"We must wait for a while," Jeremy said. "Maybe we can see him."

Jamie stared at the prison. There were cage-like rooms in front. Prisoners stood in them. They whined, "A penny! A penny!" They held out their hands to beg. "A farthing, boy! Please give a poor debtor money to buy food!"

Jamie had only one farthing. He gave the coin to one prisoner. Some of the men were very dirty. Their hair was matted, and they looked wild. They yelled and screamed.

At last a redcoat came out.

"There's one of the bailiff's men!" Jamie exclaimed. He ran over to him. "Please, sir—is Mr. Penn going to have to stay here?"

"To be sure, lad. That's why we brought him."

"Oh, no!" Jamie cried. He looked at the prisoners in the cages. "Will he——"

"No fear. William Penn won't be with them," the redcoat said, "nor yet in the inside rooms with no windows. He'll have one of those fine rooms up there."

The man pointed to the barred windows of the upper stories. Jamie glanced up.

"I wish we could see him. Perhaps there'd be something we could do for him."

"That's easy." The man pounded on the gate. "Visitors for Mr. Penn," he yelled to the guard.

When the guard opened the gate, the redcoat pointed toward the boys. Jamie could not help shuddering as the gate clanged shut behind him.

Another guard led them across a courtyard, up stairs, down an evil-smelling passage, and finally into an outside room. Some light came through the barred windows.

Mr. Penn sat on a bed with his head in his hands.

"Mr. Penn," Jeremy said, "Mr. Bell sent us to follow you. Is there anything we can do?"

The gentleman looked up. "Why, it's Jeremy Tickle," he said. "Thee is surely welcome, lad, and thy friend."

"I'm James Oglethorpe, sir. I met you several weeks ago."

Mr. Penn looked at Jamie keenly. "Oh, yes. I'm in a sad state to greet the son of my old friend." Mr. Penn added, "How is thy mother? I admire her very greatly."

"Even in all this trouble," Jamie thought, "Mr. Penn remembers to be polite." Aloud, he said, "My Lady Mother is fine, sir. She'll be sorry to know that you are here. Isn't there something we can do?"

Mr. Penn hesitated a moment. "Thee knows the way to my house, Jeremy? Thee could take a note to my wife?"

"Yes, sir. I take bread there."

Mr. Penn took out a pocket notebook and wrote rapidly. "I gave a beggar the little money I had in my moneybag," he said, as he folded the paper. "I had none left to pay a messenger."

"I will go with Jeremy to take it," said Jamie.

124

"What else can we do, sir?" asked Jeremy.

Mr. Penn smiled at the boy's troubled face. "Thee must not worry about me, lad," he said. "In a few months I will have money coming in, for my tenants will be paying their rents. Then I can pay my debts."

"But, sir, to have to stay here!" Jamie exclaimed.

"It is bad, James, but it could be worse. My wife will send me food and books. I can always think, pray, make plans, and write. I will keep busy."

The boys ran through the dark streets quickly.

Mrs. Penn was worried because her husband had not come home. "Thank you, lads, for bringing the note," she said. "You had better run home. Your mothers will be as worried as I was."

Mr. Penn stayed in Fleet Street Prison for nine months. Jamie went with Jeremy to visit him. Jeremy took fresh bread, and Jamie took apples.

Mr. Penn told them stories of his colony Pennsylvania, of America, and of the Indians who lived there.

As the boys left, Mr. Penn said to Jamie, "Thank thy mother for the books and for the food she has sent from time to time. My Lady Oglethorpe will never desert her friends. Thank you both again, lads, for your gifts."

Jamie Grows Up

ONE DAY in the fall, Jamie and Granby were walking home together. Granby saw a big rat run across the street. Quickly he made the gesture of shooting an arrow from a bow. "Twang!" he shouted. "That's the end of a wild beast."

Jamie agreed. "A city beast, but wild. Granby, when I was at Westbrook Place last summer, I tried Timothy Cason's bow. He has one longer than this." He measured as far as his arms could reach.

Granby was interested. "That must be a longbow. We have some in the armor room at Belvoir that were once used in battle. Some are so heavy

I can hardly lift them. I doubt if I could ever shoot them."

"Cason is making me a bow and some arrows," Jamie said. "I'm going to learn to shoot when we go back to Westbrook Place."

"I have some bows in town," said Granby. "So has Digby. I say, Jamie, next holiday let's get Digby and go out in the country where we can practice archery. You can use one of my bows. I'll teach you."

"Yes, let's. I'd like to. Let's take Castell and Butler, too."

Richard Butler was a new boy at school. His mother, Lady Mary Butler, was a friend of Lady Oglethorpe.

"The Butlers have lived mostly in Ireland and France," Lady Oglethorpe had told Jamie. "They've come to England because Richard is an heir of his uncle, the Duke of Ormonde. I hope you will be his friend."

Dick Butler was a year older than Jamie, but they were in the same form in school. Jamie and his friends all liked the Irish boy.

When the five boys went out for their day of archery, Jamie was surprised to find that it was so hard to handle a longbow. He had not realized how much Cason had been helping him. He was disappointed that he hit the target so seldom. The bowstring twanged his left wrist till it was red and sore.

At forty feet Granby and Digby hit the four-foot target almost every time. Butler was even better. He scored every time at fifty feet.

Even Castell showed some skill, but he did not care much about archery. Soon he dropped out. He found a bare spot of ground and, with a sharp stick, drew pictures in the earth.

The boys showed Jamie the right stance and the right way to hold the arrow and to slip the fingers off the string to release the arrow. Then they paid little more attention to him. Sometimes one said, "Stand straight, Oglethorpe," or "Watch out for that wrist," or "Better luck next time."

Jamie watched them intently. Archery looked so easy! Stand with your feet apart, your left side toward the target. Adjust the arrow to the center of the string. Draw the string back tautly. Sight along the arrow to the gold circle in the middle of the target. Let go!

The boys all had fun. They agreed to come back again to practice. A few weeks later, Theo Oglethorpe went to Westbrook Place on business. He brought back the bow and arrows Cason had whittled. Grubble made Jamie a target but could give him no advice about archery. Theo wasn't interested.

Jamie practiced every time he had a chance.

"You get better every time we go out, Jamie," Dick Butler said. "You'll beat us all soon."

In the late spring Jamie made top score. "Archery is great fun no matter who wins," he told Grubble, "but it's fun to win, too."

On their archery expeditions Jamie and Butler and Granby talked about what they would do when they grew up. They all planned to be soldiers. Three afternoons a week that winter they went to a special school to learn to use swords and to shoot pistols. With teachers to correct each fault, Jamie found that it was easier to learn how to use swords and pistols than it was to learn to use the bow and arrows.

It was a busy year. Many days Jamie saw his mother and sisters only during his early morning visit.

When summer came, Lady Oglethorpe called him to her sitting room one night. She said, "Jamie, I've decided to give up the London house for a year. All the girls are going to France. I shall travel with them and stay there several months. You must study with Mr. Purley in the country this winter. Will you mind very much, dear? You shall go to Eton as a boarding student the next year."

Jamie smiled at his lovely mother. "I'll miss you and the girls," he said politely, "and of course I'll miss the boys at school. If I can't stay in London, I'd rather go to Westbrook Place than France."

At Westbrook Place Jamie quickly became interested again in all that happened on the estate. He was especially pleased to see how well his orange trees had grown. He told Cason so.

Cason shook his head. "It be a might of work to keep 'em covered in winter. They had blooms last year but no fruit yet."

"I'll cover them this year," Jamie said.

He packed great heaps of leaves around the trunks. Then he hung awnings from the wall to protect the trees.

The first day at home Jamie had gone out to the stable. "Tofts," he said, "Sandy is getting old. I need a faster horse."

"I've got a fine one for you, Master Jamie," Tofts said. "Daniel, put a saddle on Selim."

While Daniel saddled the horse, Jamie asked, "What's happened to the boys who lived near the quarry?"

"They have a good house at last," Tofts said. "Buss works on that farm, and Little Un helps the stableman with the horses. He likes horses, that boy does."

Daniel led out a spirited young horse. Selim seemed hard to control.

"Better keep on the farm lanes for a week or so," Tofts advised.

After a few days Jamie decided, "I can handle Selim now. I wonder what sort of jumper he is?"

He spurred Selim into a run and guided the horse toward a hedge around a field. He

shortened the reins and leaned forward. "Up, Selim!"

Selim cleared the hedge neatly. Jamie was jolted, but he had stayed on. "I need practice," he said to himself. He rode across the field and jumped the hedge on the other side. He was pleased with the way Selim took the jumps.

Now that he could ride cross-country, Jamie could again ride wherever he wished. He visited Mr. Elliott and Lord Carew often. His year at Westbrook passed quickly.

The next fall, as his mother had promised, Jamie went to Eton College. It was a famous old school for boys. Both of Jamie's brothers had gone there.

One afternoon, during the study hour, Jamie was busy writing. Mr. Kennett, the master of Jamie's form, paused beside him. "Oglethorpe, are you studying?"

Jamie stood up. "Sir, I've prepared my lessons

for tomorrow. I'm just making lists of the battles the Duke of Marlborough has won for England and the generals who've served with him."

For ten years Marlborough had been commander of the English army and England's Dutch and Austrian allies. They were waging war against France.

"A good idea, Oglethorpe. Writing down facts often helps one to learn and remember them. It is good for a man to keep a commonplace book, in which he can record the things to which he may wish to refer again. Especially a man of action who is called on to think quickly and accurately will find it helpful. You plan to be a soldier, don't you, Oglethorpe?"

"Yes, sir."

"All Englishmen are proud of Marlborough's victories, of course, but a good English soldier should know more than the names of the victories. He needs to know *how* victories were won. Study the tactics of famous generals, Oglethorpe. A soldier today can still learn much from Caesar."

"Yes, sir."

As Mr. Kennett walked away, young Oglethorpe opened his Latin books obediently but with a sigh. At Eton College the masters believed all knowledge had been put down by the ancient Greek and Latin writers.

Jamie and the Generals

LADY OGLETHORPE was back in London now. Jamie went there to spend his Christmas holidays.

"How grown-up you look!" his mother exclaimed, as Jamie greeted her. She added, "I think you should have a curled wig, as well as a new suit, this year. You shall go with me to Court on the Queen's birthday. Since you are now fifteen, you must begin to take part in London society!"

Everyone was in London, it seemed, for the holidays. Jamie and Dick Butler met Granby in Piccadilly Circle. "Granby!" Jamie cried, "I didn't know you were in the army. How fine you look in uniform!"

Granby swaggered a little to show off his red coat trimmed with gold braid and his sword. "I made the campaign as an aide last summer," he said. "Now the troops are in winter quarters, so I got leave to come home."

The war with France had dragged on for ten years because armies fought only in warm weather. That was the only time they could march easily or keep their supply lines open. Both armies usually went into winter quarters when the weather turned cold and rainy.

There were loud cries in the street. "Huzza! Huzza! Huzza for the Duke!"

Two gray horses trotted down the street. They were pulling an open carriage. In the carriage sat a stern-faced man, who wore a wig with long white curls. He bowed to the people as he passed.

"Here comes Marlborough," said Granby with a sniff. "Listen to the cheers!"

"You don't like the Duke, do you?" asked Jamie. "Why not? Isn't he a great general?"

"He may be," Granby admitted. "He knows how to plan a campaign and lead men in a battle, but he has such a mean spirit. He never praises anyone but his friends."

Jamie frowned. "I've always wanted to see the Duke of Marlborough because I thought he was a great hero. Now Theo says he's been accused of taking for himself money that should have bought food for his army."

"I don't believe he did that," Granby said slowly. His eyes brightened. "You should see Prince Eugene, the Austrian general. He's the one the soldiers admire. He is really a hero!"

Many people in England were angry at the Duke of Marlborough. Some said he had made himself the richest man in Europe. Others said he wanted to keep England at war with France so he could get even richer. On the last day of 1711, Queen Anne dismissed him from her army. She named the Duke of Ormonde to be Captain-General in his place.

Jamie told his mother, "Next summer Dick Butler will be an aide to his uncle. May I make the campaign, too?"

"No," Lady Oglethorpe said firmly. "You are still too young."

In January, Granby's hero, Prince Eugene, came to London. All the soldiers on leave praised the Austrian general. They called him the bravest man in all Europe. Soldiers declared they would follow him to the ends of the earth.

Jamie came into his mother's room in great excitement one January morning.

"Lady Mother," he said, "Prince Eugene is to have dinner with the Duke of Ormonde tomorrow, and the Duke has invited Dick and me."

Lady Oglethorpe was pleased. "I am glad you can meet the Prince. He is truly a hero to admire."

The Duke of Ormonde had invited a dozen men to his dinner party. When the boys came in, he led them over to his famous guest. "Your Highness," he said, "here are two young men who admire you greatly. May I present my nephew, Richard Butler, and my young friend, James Oglethorpe?"

To Jamie's surprise the great hero was a small man. Prince Eugene looked even smaller than the Englishmen, because he wore no wig. His light brown hair was tied with a ribbon at the back of his neck.

The boys made deep bows. Prince Eugene's bow was as polite as theirs. His manners made Jamie feel like a man, not a schoolboy.

"Your Highness," he said, "England is honored to have you as a guest. We hope you like our country."

"I do, indeed," the Prince answered with a smile. "I find I have many friends here."

"My father and my brother were soldiers, Your Highness," Jamie said. "I hope to be one also."

"And so do I, sir," Richard added. "My uncle will take me as his aide next summer."

The Prince looked at the boys with sharp eyes. "I am sure you will be fine soldiers," he said. "Your country has many. I am honored to command beside the Duke of Ormonde, as I have been honored to serve with the Duke of Marlborough."

The gentleman nearest the Prince said, with a laugh, "Oh, Your Highness! Perhaps the Duke of Marlborough had the good luck to be fortunate once or twice on the field of battle!"

There was a hint of anger in the Prince's voice when he answered quickly, "That is truly a compliment to the Duke. He may sometimes have been fortunate. He was always successful."

Jamie had wondered what the Prince thought of Marlborough. He was glad the gentleman had mentioned the Duke.

Jamie remembered the Prince's answer. It was polite. It was well worded. It told the man who laughed that the Prince would allow no one to criticize the Duke of Marlborough in his presence.

Jamie told Granby about it later. "No gentleman there would speak well of Marlborough, now that he is no longer in command. Prince Eugene, however, is loyal. He has a quick mind as well as courage and honor. Now I know why you admire him so much."

Christmas holidays lasted through the Queen's birthday on February sixth. On that day Jamie got dressed to go to Court as Lady Oglethorpe had planned.

He was proud of his new suit of dark blue velvet with large silver buttons. He had a richly embroidered waistcoat to wear with his new suit. The new wig with long white curls felt strange and heavy on his head.

"No one will recognize me today. I don't even know myself," he complained to old Nurse Middlecase. She had come to admire her "baby" in his grown-up clothes. "And I am sure to trip over my sword."

"No, you won't," Nannie assured him. "Just

remember you are James Edward Oglethorpe of Westbrook Place."

A maid knocked at the door of Jamie's room. "Master James, Lady Oglethorpe says to hurry! The carriage is at the door."

Jamie rushed out and ran down the stairs. Nannie looked after him proudly. "When he was a little boy he used to wish he could be one of King Arthur's knights," she said. "He'll be the finest gentleman in the family, I wager."

There was a great swarm of carriages driving up to the palace. Some people even had new carriages for the occasion. Everyone had new and very fine clothes to celebrate Queen Anne's birthday.

Inside the great reception rooms, there were many people and much talk. Over and over Jamie made his bow as his mother presented him to her friends. Soon he forgot to worry about tripping over his sword, but the wig still felt heavy and hot on his head.

"I hear the Queen is not well," a gentleman told Lady Oglethorpe. "She may not make an appearance today."

"Oh, but she must!" Jamie cried before his mother could speak. "Isn't she to present a fine sword to Prince Eugene?"

Everyone at Court today had been talking about the sword. The hilt was said to be set with diamonds and other precious gems.

Just then a herald blew his trumpet. When the crowd grew quiet, he announced, "Prince Eugene, Commander of the Austrian army."

People drew back to make space for him to pass through the rooms. The Prince, with an English gentleman beside him, walked down this aisle. He looked very serious today.

Queen Anne did appear, to present the sword. From a distance Jamie could see her. He saw Prince Eugene bow as he received the gift, but he could not hear what was said. A few minutes later the Queen left the reception room.

The Prince was surrounded by admirers. Jamie joined the group, but he hesitated to speak to the Prince. Then Eugene saw him. "Ah, young Oglethorpe, it is a pleasure to see you again."

Jamie was very much pleased. The Prince had remembered him! "I wish Your Highness even greater success with your new sword," he said.

The New Soldier

THE NEXT fall Jamie began his second year at Eton. One day he received a message from his mother. Lady Oglethorpe was now at Windsor Castle, near Eton. She was one of Queen Anne's ladies-in-waiting.

Her note said:

Get permission to come to the Castle at three tomorrow afternoon. Meet me at the gate of the rose garden.

Jamie was at the gate at the dot of three. Queen Anne was walking in the sunshine. Jamie gazed at her as his mother led him forward. The Queen was a very fat woman and she looked ill.

149

But she held her head high. She looked—she looked like a Queen!

A few feet away Lady Oglethorpe stopped and made a low curtsy. Jamie bowed.

"Your Majesty," said Lady Oglethorpe, "may I present my son James Edward? He is still in Eton, but he hopes for a place in Your Majesty's Guards."

Queen Anne looked sharply at Jamie for several seconds. Then she nodded. "He is a well-formed youth," she observed, "and he has the manners of a gentleman. England has need of many strong young men."

She held out her hand, palm down. Jamie dropped to one knee to kiss it. "Your Majesty," he said, "I will serve you and England with my life."

Queen Anne studied him a little longer. She smiled. "We will order your commission." Then she turned to Lady Oglethorpe. "Madam, you will want to visit with your son. You may be dismissed."

When they had left the Queen's presence Lady Oglethorpe told her son, "I think you are still too young to have a commission in the army. Since the Queen is a very sick woman, she may not live long. She is my friend and I want your commission to be signed by her."

"Thank you very much, Lady Mother, for asking her," said Jamie. "Shall I leave school at once?"

"Oh, no! Of course not, dear. The army will soon be in winter quarters. Perhaps you may go as an aide to the Duke of Ormonde next summer."

In 1713 England and France signed a peace treaty. Young Lieutenant Oglethorpe was not needed in the army. That year he stayed at Eton. The next spring he entered the University of Oxford.

Queen Anne died in the summer of 1714. She left no child, so the Parliament had to choose the heir to her throne. Two princes had claims. One was the Queen's nephew, Prince James. He lived in France. It was his mother with whom the Oglethorpe girls lived as ladies-in-waiting.

The other was the late Queen's cousin, Prince George of Hanover, a German state. It was Prince George that the men in Parliament chose to be King of England.

The Oglethorpes were greatly disappointed. They had all hoped that Prince James would become King James III of England. The Oglethorpes had always been loyal to him. If he were King, the family could hope to have important places at Court.

Theo especially was very angry. "I won't live in England," he declared. "I can't be the loyal subject of a German King. Why, he doesn't even speak English!"

152

"But, Theo," Jamie protested, "you're a Member of Parliament and the master of Westbrook Place!" Jamie knew that since his father's death their country home had belonged to the eldest son—first Lewis and now Theo.

"You can have Westbrook," Theo answered. "You like it, and I never want to live there again."

"I'm afraid you are not being very wise," said Lady Oglethorpe. "There is always a chance that many English people may grow to dislike King George. English people have driven kings they hated from the throne before this. If that should happen, I am sure Prince James would become King."

"Then I'll return to England with him in triumph," Theo said. "I'll go to him now to prove that I am loyal only to him."

Jamie's commission as an officer in the Guards had been renewed by King George, but Jamie had never been assigned to a post.

After Theo went to France, Jamie felt very restless at Oxford. He found it hard to study. Like his brother, he could not feel entirely loyal to this new king.

"Lady Mother," he suggested, "I'd like to go to France. I could study in Paris."

Lady Oglethorpe hesitated. "That may be a good plan," she agreed finally. "You will see your sisters there, and it is good for a young man to travel."

Jamie wondered if she thought he would go to Prince James as Theo had. "I don't think I will," Jamie thought. "I am Oglethorpe of Westbrook Place now and England, not France, is my home."

Jamie was restless in France, too. He decided: "I want to be a soldier. The greatest general in the world is Prince Eugene. Now he is fighting the Turks who have invaded Europe. I'll go to him, and learn to be a soldier."

He left France without telling anyone.

Prince Eugene remembered young Oglethorpe. "I shall be glad to have you as my aide," he said.

Jamie toured the camps with the Prince. He carried orders. He helped draw maps. He learned to shoot cannon and to drill troops.

"You learn fast, Oglethorpe," Prince Eugene told him. "You will make a good officer."

One night in the officers' dining hall Oglethorpe was talking excitedly of a new cannon. "When we learn to handle it right," he said, "I believe it will knock a hole right through the great stone wall around the city. Then we can drive the Turks out!"

The Prince of Württemberg sat opposite Jamie. "Our eager young Oglethorpe looks warm," he said lazily. "Perhaps this will cool him down."

He spun his water goblet. The goblet was

almost empty, but some drops hit Jamie's face. This rude act was an insult. Several officers laughed. That was insulting too.

Jamie's temper flared. He jumped up with his hand on the hilt of his sword. He wanted to challenge the Prince to a duel, but it was bad for a young officer to get the reputation of being quarrelsome.

Yet if he did nothing, the officers would think him a coward. Everyone was watching.

Jamie forced a friendly smile to his lips. "That is a good joke, Your Highness," he said pleasantly, "but in England we do it better."

He lifted a full goblet and threw all the water into the Prince's face. With a bow and a smile he sat down. Let the Prince of Württemberg be the one to start a quarrel.

There was a burst of laughter from the other officers. "Good turn to the joke, Oglethorpe," one called.

An older officer talked to Jamie as they left the dining hall. "You showed a clever wit to turn the joke, Oglethorpe," he said, "but the Prince is very angry now."

"I'm not afraid to have him challenge me to a duel," Jamie answered stubbornly.

"I don't think he will," the older man replied. "The Prince of Württemberg is too proud to fight a duel with a man who has no title. He has more pride than he has wit."

A few weeks later the Prince went home. It was more important to him to keep his pride and dignity than to be a good officer.

The siege of Belgrade began. The Turks had made a fortress of the city of Belgrade. "We must drive them out now or never," Prince Eugene said. "A large army is on the way to aid them."

Prince Eugene kept Oglethorpe busy carrying orders and bringing back reports.

"Your Highness," Oglethorpe said to the Prince after he had made one report, "the officer attacking the wall near the west gate must have been killed. As I passed, the men were in disorder. Shall I take his place?"

Prince Eugene also liked to be in the forefront of action. He looked sharply at Jamie. "Yes, go," he said.

Jamie found the men fleeing in little groups. A band of Turks had come out of the city to pursue them.

Jamie rode rapidly from group to group. "To the edge of the wood!" he commanded. "We shall re-form there and turn to attack."

His decision and coolness gave the men courage. At the edge of the wood they grouped together and prepared to fight again.

The Turks were riding hard toward them. The Turks thought their enemies were fleeing into the woods. They did not stop to fire their

guns. They meant to cut the men down with swords.

"Ready! Fire!" Oglethorpe ordered.

The sudden shots stopped the Turks. Some fell from their horses. A few took aim and fired.

"Attack!" Oglethorpe shouted. He spurred his horse and rode toward the Turkish leader. The men followed him. The surprised Turks turned and raced toward the gate. Only a few made it.

The west gate was not so well defended now. Oglethorpe and his men made a breach. There was much hard fighting, but the city fell to Prince Eugene's army six days later.

The Prince praised Oglethorpe. "You showed remarkable skill and courage in leading your men." Then he added, "I shall see that you are well rewarded."

When the troops went into winter quarters, Prince Eugene gave Oglethorpe a share of the spoils from the captured city. "I should like to keep you as an officer," the Prince said. "Will you stay?"

"No thank you, Your Highness," answered Oglethorpe. "I appreciate what you have taught me, but I cannot stay. When I fight again, it will be against the enemies of England."

The Colony in Georgia

BACK in England, young Colonel Oglethorpe became the Squire of Westbrook Place. He had had enough of fighting for a while. He decided to go into politics. The Oglethorpes of Westbrook Place had always felt it was the duty of gentlemen to serve in the government of England. James Oglethorpe's father and two brothers had all been Members of Parliament. In 1722 he was elected for the same district.

At a reception a few years later Lady Oglethorpe met an old friend, the Duke of Argyle. He was one of King George's closest advisers.

"I want to congratulate you on the speech your

son James made in the House of Commons recently," the Duke said. "He speaks well, and he thinks well. He made a good argument for sending a number of German settlers to the colonies in America."

"My son will appreciate your praise," Lady Oglethorpe replied. "He is greatly concerned about those poor people. So many have had to leave their own country. If they can't accept the same religion as their rulers, they are driven from their homes. My son believes, like William Penn, that every man should be free to practice his own faith."

"He isn't here tonight?"

"No, he's at home. He's preparing another speech. He is studying all the laws that England has made about trade with the colonies. Jamie feels he must know everything about a subject before he makes a speech."

"Is he always so thorough?" asked the Duke.

"Always," Lady Oglethorpe answered proudly. "Whatever he does, whether it's learning to shoot or manage a farm or make a speech, he does his very best."

One day in 1729 a man stopped Oglethorpe as he was going into a coffeehouse.

"I say, aren't you James Oglethorpe? Do you remember me? I'm Thomas Baston."

"Why, Baston, the cock of our form! How are you?"

Baston suggested that they sit together in the coffeehouse. They talked about old school friends and school days.

Oglethorpe laughed as he remembered his two fights with Baston. "I used to think you were a bully," he said.

"I expect I was," Baston agreed. "I liked to fight, but I never held grudges." He drank his coffee. "I wonder if you know Robin Castell is in Fleet Street Prison for debt?"

"Castell!" Oglethorpe was shocked. "I thought he was abroad. I haven't seen him since his book on the Villas of the Ancients was published a few years ago. Is the debt very large? I want to help him."

"No, the debt was small," said Baston. "Robin's been too proud to ask his friends for help."

Oglethorpe glanced at the coffeehouse clock. He got up hastily. "I'm due at a committee meeting soon," he said, "but I'll stop on my way to see Robin."

Oglethorpe found that poor Robin Castell had been unlucky. The jailer of Fleet Street Prison was a cruel man. He had put Castell in a cell with men who had smallpox. Robin had died just before Oglethorpe arrived.

Oglethorpe visited the wretched men crowded in the cells. Many of them were sick. He talked to some of them. He saw the dirt and the misery and the cruelty. He saw a guard take a gift of

food and begin to sell it. Oglethorpe tried to stop the guard, but the jailer just laughed at him.

When Oglethorpe left the prison, he was very angry. "I never saw such cruelty and misery as there are in that prison," he said to himself. "There's no more reason for many of those men to be there than there was for Robin."

A single Englishman could do nothing to change conditions, but there was a way that he might help. He was a Member of Parliament.

Working late that night, Oglethorpe drew up a bill to present the next day. Parliament took action. Oglethorpe was made chairman, of a committee to investigate conditions in all the London prisons.

The committee learned many things. The debtors' prisons were overcrowded. The jailers were not paid much, so they were kind to men whose friends could give them bribes. The poor prisoners got very little to eat. The guards laughed to see them fight over scraps of food. Everything was very dirty. The prisoners had to sleep on musty straw. The air was so full of stinking odors that it was difficult to breathe.

For several years Oglethorpe spent most of his time working for the debtors. He tried to get justice for people who were not criminals. He tried to get more merciful treatment for the criminals. Oglethorpe talked with a lawyer, Sir Joseph Jekyll, about ways to correct the evils.

"You know, Sir Joseph, most of these men aren't criminals at all. Most of them are in prison because they are hard up and cannot pay their debts. Some are fine men, as well educated as Robin Castell or William Penn."

"It's a pity Mr. Penn has died," Sir Joseph said. "He helped many poor men get to his colony in America."

"I could pay to send a few men myself," said Oglethorpe, "but there are so many who need a place to go. Anyway the colonies object when we try to send more poor families to them."

"Many people might give money to found a new colony, if you can organize a company and secure a large grant of land in America," Sir Joseph suggested.

That night Oglethorpe got out a map of America. He studied the coast line from Massachusetts down through the Carolinas to Florida. His eyes brightened. Florida belonged to Spain. Spain had soldiers there who threatened to attack South Carolina and to take that colony away from England. England and Spain both claimed the land between the Savannah and the St. Johns rivers. No white settlers lived there.

"Why," Oglethorpe exclaimed aloud, "here is the place! England needs soldiers south of the Carolinas. Our poor friends now in prison would make good soldiers if they had homes for which

to fight. This land is in a warm climate. England will never be able to grow oranges or olives or tropical friuts. A colony here might cultivate them. This country might even be a good place to grow silkworms! England needs silk thread so she won't have to buy silks from Italy and China."

Oglethorpe grew very excited over his project. He organized the Corporation for Establishing Charitable Colonies in America. He persuaded important and wealthy men to act as Trustees. They helped him raise money and make plans for the colony. They petitioned King George for land.

He also went to see another old school friend, Edward Digby. He belonged now to a society that supported Christian missionaries.

"Digby," Oglethorpe said, "I wish you would serve as one of the Trustees. We need you."

"I'd be glad to," Digby said. "I think my society will give some money to your project. We are very much interested in what you are trying to do. Later we'll send missionaries to the Indians there."

"Excellent," Oglethorpe answered. "It's very important to make the Indians our friends. Your missionaries should help us."

King George approved the plans for the new colony. He granted the Trustees a charter. It gave them the land between the Savannah and the Altamaha rivers, the Atlantic Ocean to the Pacific. In honor of the King the Trustees named the colony Georgia.

Poor men began to hear about the new colony. Many who came to Oglethorpe begged to take their families to Georgia. Many had never been in debtors' prison, but they felt they had little chance to make a good living in England.

Oglethorpe studied their applications. Georgia was still a wilderness. It was important to send just the right men in the first group of colonists. Many of them must be men of special skills.

The men who went in the very first ship were to include a surveyor to measure the land, carpenters to build houses, cabinetmakers to make furniture, farmers, gardeners, a baker, a minister, a doctor, a man to prepare medicines, and as many other trained workers as possible. Every man must be honest and hard-working. He must be healthy, and he must be willing to serve as a soldier.

"I don't think we shall have to fight the Indians," Oglethorpe told the Trustees. "Mr. Penn showed that it is possible to keep the Indians' friendship. We may have trouble with Spain. There is a strong Spanish fort at St. Augustine in Florida. The Spanish insist all North America belongs to them. I am convinced our explorers claimed it for England first. We must be prepared to fight if Spain fights us."

"We must not let our men provoke the Spaniards," one of the Trustees warned him. "Remember we are sending men to farm, not to be soldiers."

"That's true," Oglethorpe agreed. "We need not cross that bridge until we come to it."

Few of the prospective settlers had furniture or tools to take with them. The Trustees had agreed that for the first year they would supply everything that was needed. They would provide food, clothing, medicines, tools, plants and seeds, as well as guns and ammunition.

Many plans had to be made. At last all was ready. On November 17, 1732, the frigate *Anne* sailed for Georgia. On board were one hundred and sixteen colonists. Forty of them were men able to bear arms. The rest were women and children. Their leader was James Oglethorpe himself.

The First Months in Georgia

WRAPPED in a great cloak, James Oglethorpe stood on the deck of the *Anne*. He was gazing toward the west. It was a sunny day, and all sails were spread to catch the steady breeze.

"Mr. Oglethorpe!" a young voice said beside him. The voice was polite, but it quivered with excitement.

Oglethorpe looked down at the black-haired boy who had spoken. "Yes, John?"

"The lookout says he can see land! Will that be Georgia, sir?"

"No, we plan to put in at Charles Town in South Carolina first." Oglethorpe stared hard at

174

the horizon. "John," he said, "run down to the cabin and get my spyglass."

Twelve-year-old John Milledge sped away. All during the voyage he had run errands for his hero.

Soon everyone could see the line of land. Then buildings and trees began to show against the sky line.

America! All the colonists crowded the side of the ship to see the land they had dreamed of! Here was the new home they had talked about during seven long weeks at sea!

Through his spyglass Oglethorpe studied the shore. "The people of Charles Town are sending a boat to greet us," he said. "Look, John! See what they are bringing!" He handed the spyglass to the boy.

"Why, they've got apples and cabbages and chickens, haven't they, sir?"

Before nightfall the *Anne* lay at anchor in the

harbor. The people on the ship feasted on fresh food that night. No more salt pork!

The next day the *Anne* sailed down the coast between sandy islands to the seaport of Beaufort. As the ship came to anchor there John Milledge asked Oglethorpe, "Is this Georgia, sir?"

Oglethorpe laughed. "No, John. There will be no houses in Georgia—until we build them."

The colonists were to stay in soldiers' barracks at Beaufort while Oglethorpe went ahead to find a place for them to build their town. The next day he and Colonel Bull from Charles Town would start out to explore the Savannah River in Georgia. Two men would go with them to row the small boat.

Just before they left Oglethorpe said, "Mr. Milledge, John is a useful boy. I'd like to take him with me."

John was already running to the boat before his father could give permission.

Eighteen miles up the river the explorers found the right place. It was on a bluff above the river. The Indian name for the bluff was Yamacraw. On it pine trees stood thick and tall. There were springs of fresh water.

Some Indians stood on the bluff, watching the little boat. James Oglethorpe made signs to show that the white men were friendly.

An Indian woman came down to the edge of the water. "Me, Mary Musgrove," she said. "Me speak English."

Oglethorpe stepped ashore. "Is your chief here?"

Mary Musgrove pointed to a tall, very dignified old man. "That he. That Tomo-chi-chi."

Oglethorpe spread his arms wide to show that he meant no harm. He took a few steps toward Tomo-chi-chi. The two men gazed at each other for a long time. Finally the Indian nodded. "Ugh!" he said in a friendly fashion.

Oglethorpe turned to Mary. "Tell him," he said, "we have come across the great waters. We want to be friends. We want to build a town under these trees. We want to trade with the Indians."

She spoke in the Indian language. Tomo-chi-chi listened. He looked at Oglethorpe a long time before he answered.

178

Mary translated his words. "He say this good land. Indians live here long time. Indians need friends. White man there—" she pointed to the south— "bad enemy to Tomo-chi-chi."

Oglethorpe nodded gravely. "Tell the great chief," he said, "the Spaniards there—" he also pointed to the south—"are our enemies, too. If they come here, we will fight them together."

After she spoke, there was silence again. "John," said Oglethorpe, "bring me the bundle in the front of the boat."

He gave the Indians gifts he had brought for them. Then they smoked together in friend-ship.

On the way back to Beaufort, Oglethorpe said to John, "Here in Georgia we must always try to be friends with the Indians. We are asking them to give us land to live on. I think they want to learn our ways, and we must help them."

John thought over this idea. "My uncle didn't

want us to come. He said the Indians would scalp us all. If we are friends, they won't, will they?"

Colonel Bull shook his head. "The Indians aren't likely to bother you much unless the Spaniards stir them up," he said, "or unless your traders try to cheat them on the furs they bring to sell."

"Cheating is always poor business," Oglethorpe said. "We need the Indians on our side against the Spaniards."

Governor Robert Johnson of South Carolina came to see Oglethorpe. "The *Anne* is too large to go up the Savannah River," he said. "We'll lend you small boats. I'll send some soldiers to guard you till your fort is built. We want to give you cattle and pigs for your farms. Do you need anything else?"

"We appreciate your gifts," Oglethorpe answered. "We do need one more thing. Can we hire some men to show us the best way to cut trees and build log houses? Our men will learn from your men."

A few days later Oglethorpe wrote to the Trustees in London:

The whole people arrived here on the 12th of February; at night their tents were got up.

The next weeks were busy. The wide streets of the town of Savannah were laid out. Trees were cut. A fort was built. Houses were going up. Fields were cleared. One street was named for Colonel Bull. A square was named for Governor Johnson.

In June Tomo-chi-chi brought eight chiefs of the Creek Indian tribes to Savannah to see Oglethorpe. These Indians feared and hated the Spaniards in Florida. They were willing to give land to the English in return for protection.

Tomo-chi-chi brought his friend Oglethorpe a buffalo skin. It was decorated with the head and feathers of an eagle.

Tomo-chi-chi spoke and Mary Musgrove told Oglethorpe what he had said. "The eagle means speed, and the buffalo, strength. The English are swift as the eagle and strong as the buffalo. Like the eagle they flew hither over great waters. Like the buffalo nothing can withstand them. But the feathers of the eagle are soft and mean kindness. The skin of the buffalo is a warm cover and means protection. Let these remind the English to be kind and protect us."

Oglethorpe was pleased with the gift. "I will always be a true friend to your people, the Creeks, and to the tribes who are your friends," he promised Tomo-chi-chi.

Every few months small boatloads of colonists arrived. By the spring of 1734, when Oglethorpe returned to England to report to the Trustees, there were eleven small towns in Georgia. More than four hundred people had come to the colony to build homes in the new land.

Plans for a Pageant

MANY, many years later Mr. Milledge of Savannah brought home an armload of books.

His nine-year-old daughter, Mary, met him at the door. "Father," she said proudly, "I learned to spell a long word today."

Mr. Milledge put his books on the table. "Fine! Let's hear you spell it."

"B-i-c-e-n-t-e-n-n-i-a-l!" Mary spelled slowly and carefully.

"Good," her father exclaimed. "Do you know what that long word means?"

"It means two hundred years. And we're going to have a birthday party!"

Mary's older brother John sat at a table drawing on a big sheet of paper. "Two-hundredth year, Mary," he corrected. "And it's a celebration, not a birthday party. Look, Father——"

"It will *too* be a birthday party," Mary interrupted crossly. "Miss Turner said so. Because Georgia will be two hundred years old. It will be a birthday party for everyone in the state."

Mr. Milledge laughed. "You are both right. We talked about it at the Georgia Historical Society meeting today."

John held up his paper. "In our room we're making a model of Savannah as it looked two hundred years ago, when the first John Milledge lived here. I'm copying the old maps you have in your study. Here are Bull Street and Johnson Square. The first church was built on this corner where Christ Church is today."

"Silly!" Mary objected. "There weren't any streets or anything when General Oglethorpe came. There were just miles and miles and miles of trees, and Indians lived here."

"Well, a hundred ninety-five years ago then," laughed John. "Look, Father, even after all the houses shown on this map were built, General Oglethorpe still lived in a tent right here on the bank of the river."

Mrs. Milledge came to the door. "Time to get ready for supper. Children, run wash your hands."

When everyone was at the table and plates were served, Mrs. Milledge said, "Guess what we were planning today at the P.T.A. meeting." But she didn't wait for them to guess. "A big pageant to celebrate Georgia's two-hundredth birthday!"

Everyone laughed. "That's what we were talking about, too," Mr. Milledge said.

"What is a pageant?" Mary asked.

"It's a kind of play," Mrs. Milledge explained,

"with short scenes showing important events. It takes a lot of people to act out all the parts. This one will start with a scene showing the great woods. General Oglethorpe and the first settlers will come in dressed as people were then. They will buy the land from the Indians."

Mary said, "The Indian chief was Tomo-chi-chi. He was General Oglethorpe's friend, and he wore feathers in his hair."

"Yes," John added, "but Tomo-chi-chi couldn't speak English. They had to have an interpreter. Mary Musgrove was a woman in Tomo-chi-chi's tribe whose father was an English trader. She told the settlers what Tomo-chi-chi said and the Indians what Oglethorpe said."

"Oglethorpe was sure he could trust his Indian friends," his father took up the story. "He got busy building forts to protect the colony from the Spaniards. He didn't worry about a palisade to keep out the Indians."

186

"Oh," cried John. "That's why the map shows just a part of a wooden palisade around the city."

After supper the family made a list of other events that might be included in the pageant.

"It should show Oglethorpe greeting the colonists who were not English," Mr. Milledge said. "There were Jews who had been persecuted in Spain, and Moravians and Salzburgers from Germany."

"Yes," agreed Mrs. Milledge, "and we must have the arrival of the brave Scots soldiers and their families. When they went south to build their town, Darien, they knew they were an outpost against the Spaniards in Florida."

Mr. Milledge added, "It was mainly the Scots who defeated the Spanish at the Battle of Bloody Marsh. After that the Spaniards were never again able to attack the colonies. That battle broke the power of Spain in the New World. There could be a grand scene showing Oglethorpe using his few men to ambush a Spanish army ten times as strong."

"Did the children go to school?" Mary asked.

"Of course," Mrs. Milledge said. "We might show the first school and the kind of books they used. Wasn't George Whitefield the first school-master?"

"I'm not sure," said Mr. Milledge, "but he built the first orphanage in America. At the town of Bethesda, in 1739, I think. You ought to show that. And I believe he started the first Sunday school, too."

"And John Wesley, the Methodist preacher," John exclaimed. "Didn't he come to Georgia to preach to the Indians?"

"Yes, he did," agreed Mrs. Milledge. "He and his brother Charles came just a year or two after the first shipload of colonists. We mustn't leave the Wesleys out."

"Did you know the Trustees hoped the colony

188

could raise tropical fruits in Georgia?" Mr. Milledge asked. "They knew the soil was good for farming, and they thought the climate would be just right for things like oranges and olives. One of the first things Oglethorpe did was set out a garden and an orchard. The Trustees sent him plants and seeds from all the tropical countries. He tried to find out which would grow best in Georgia. They called it the Trustees' Garden."

"Oh, the Garden Clubs would like to work on that," said Mrs. Milledge. "I didn't realize how fitting it is that the first Garden Club in America was started in Georgia. General Oglethorpe would have been pleased about that, don't you think?"

"What about silkworms?" John asked. "Our history book said they tried to grow silkworms and make silk right here."

Mr. Milledge agreed. "Yes, General Oglethorpe brought some Italian families to teach the

settlers how to feed the worms on the native mulberry leaves and how to unwind the silk fibers from the cocoons. The silk industry was important work when the colony was new and continued to be for many years. I think that should be included."

John had picked up a book from the table. "Listen to this," he exclaimed. He read aloud: "'Mr. Oglethorpe is extremely well beloved by all his People: The general Title they give him, is FATHER: If any of them is sick, he immediately visits them and takes a great deal of Care of them: If any Difference arises, he's the Person that decides it. He keeps a strict Discipline. In short He has done a vast deal of Work for the Time; and, I think, his NAME justly deserves to *be Immortalized.'*"

"Yes, I've seen that," said Mr. Milledge. "A visitor from South Carolina first published it in his paper in 1733. He was right, too. General

Oglethorpe's name does deserve to rank with the great heroes of all time. He is Georgia's first and perhaps her greatest hero."

Mr. Milledge thought a moment and then went on, speaking slowly. "No one man can do everything. It was General Oglethorpe's work to found a colony where unfortunate men could have a chance to make a good life for their families, and to defend the colony from the Spaniards. He did a good job. For ten years he gave all his time and most of his fortune to make a success of the colony. Then he went back to England, and other men took up the task of making Georgia a great state."

"What a wonderful pageant we can have," John said. "Father, I'm glad our ancestors settled here. It's great to be a Georgian, isn't it?"

INDIANS

POCAHONTAS, *Seymour*
SACAGAWEA, *Seymour*
SITTING BULL, *Stevenson*
TECUMSEH, *Stevenson*

NAVAL HEROES

DAVID FARRAGUT, *Long*
GEORGE DEWEY, *Long*
JOHN PAUL JONES, *Snow*
MATTHEW CALBRAITH PERRY, *Scharbach*
OLIVER HAZARD PERRY, *Long*
RAPHAEL SEMMES, *Snow*
STEPHEN DECATUR, *Smith*

NOTED WIVES and MOTHERS

ABIGAIL ADAMS, *Wagoner*
DOLLY MADISON, *Monsell*
JESSIE FREMONT, *Wagoner*
MARTHA WASHINGTON, *Wagoner*
MARY TODD LINCOLN, *Wilkie*
NANCY HANKS, *Stevenson*
RACHEL JACKSON, *Govan*

SCIENTISTS and INVENTORS

ALECK BELL, *Widdemer*
ELI WHITNEY, *Snow*
GEORGE CARVER, *Stevenson*
GEORGE EASTMAN, *Henry*
HENRY FORD, *Aird-Ruddiman*
JOHN AUDUBON, *Mason*
LUTHER BURBANK, *Burt*
MARIA MITCHELL, *Melin*
ROBERT FULTON, *Henry*
SAMUEL MORSE, *Snow*
TOM EDISON, *Guthridge*
WALTER REED, *Higgins*
WILBUR AND ORVILLE WRIGHT, *Stevenson*
WILL AND CHARLIE MAYO, *Hammontree*

SOCIAL and CIVIC LEADERS

BETSY ROSS, *Weil*
BOOKER T. WASHINGTON, *Stevenson*
CLARA BARTON, *Stevenson*
DAN BEARD, *Mason*
JANE ADDAMS, *Wagoner*
JULIA WARD HOWE, *Wagoner*
JULIETTE LOW, *Higgins*
LUCRETIA MOTT, *Burnett*
MOLLY PITCHER, *Stevenson*
SUSAN ANTHONY, *Monsell*

SOLDIERS

ANTHONY WAYNE, *Stevenson*
BEDFORD FORREST, *Parks*
DAN MORGAN, *Bryant*
ETHAN ALLAN, *Winders*
FRANCIS MARION, *Steele*
ISRAEL PUTNAM, *Stevenson*
JEB STUART, *Winders*
NATHANAEL GREENE, *Peckham*
ROBERT E. LEE, *Monsell*
TOM JACKSON, *Monsell*
U. S. GRANT, *Stevenson*
WILLIAM HENRY HARRISON, *Peckham*
ZACK TAYLOR, *Wilkie*

STATESMEN

ABE LINCOLN, *Stevenson*
ANDY JACKSON, *Stevenson*
DAN WEBSTER, *Smith*
FRANKLIN ROOSEVELT, *Weil*
HENRY CLAY, *Monsell*
JAMES MONROE, *Widdemer*
JOHN MARSHALL, *Monsell*
SAM HOUSTON, *Stevenson*
TEDDY ROOSEVELT, *Parks*
WOODROW WILSON, *Monsell*

Library
of

Oglethorpe College

RARE BOOKS

NESCIT CEDERE

James Oglethorpe Collection